SUMMERLAND

by

Leo Bonomo

CON-PSY PUBLICATIONS

Bless you
Savour
light always
Leo xxx

First Edition

© Leo Bonomo
2014

Published by
CON-PSY PUBLICATIONS

P.O. BOX 14,
GREENFORD,
MIDDLESEX, UB6 0UF.

ISBN 978 1 898680 64 2

SUMMERLAND

Foreword

'SUMMERLAND' is a most unusual book. It is written by Spirit, those whom we may call 'Guardian Angels' and has been written specifically as a NOVEL. This is the very first time this has been done.

It has been written as a novel for a special purpose, so that this simple story of life, the change (Death) and our eternal existence may be told. Its aim is to express the fact that there is more to us than some of us would like to acknowledge, but it is something that more and more of us are beginning to believe in and understand. Man has an inherent knowledge that something else exists - a God, or Creator, whichever name we give it.

Our Guardian Angels wrote it this way so that our children may also learn of God from a source that complements what most people believe -that there is a Creator, a God, that there is hope and for most, peace after the change.

Our Guardian Angels do not want to change your minds; you have freewill. They just want to make you aware, so that you may make more informed choices about the way you live this life.

'SUMMERLAND' explores what happens and why. It shows, through its simple story, what form life in the next world takes and most importantly, why we must all finally, take responsibility for not only our actions and inactions but also the thoughts and intentions behind them.

May the great Creator Bless you All.

This book is dedicated to all the poor and suffering peoples of the world. It is also dedicated to those in the Spirit World, especially to my helpers and guides in the next world and of course, to the Great Creator.

"Subatomic or quantum physics has provided us with concepts that make the existence of psychic phenomena entirely and rationally plausible - indeed, likely! - and furthermore validate belief in continuing discarnate existence of the individual discarnate soul in the afterlife." Dr Howard Jones Author.

- Have you have ever wondered what it was like to die?
- Or perhaps how Mediums work?
- What it is like in the Spirit World?
- What is Karma and how it works?
- What are the real unfailing laws pertaining to us? The laws we cannot ever cheat. The laws of Cause & Effect. What is the real retribution for evil doing?
- Have you ever wondered, also, about what it might be like to be born?
- What is a reason for cot deaths?
- Perhaps even why we are here at all?
- How and why people become taken over, possessed by other spirits?
- Why is there so much evil in this world today?

Depending on your viewpoint, you will find many answers within these pages. This book has been written entirely by automatic writing. Written, some may say, by an unseen hand.

What would its purpose be? While some may say answers are not found within these pages, it will surely give cause for thought to those questions posed.

Always search for the truth.

A journey we shall all take at some point.
Not only the journey of a lifetime...
But a journey of an existence...
So many dream of 'living forever'.
Not understanding that we do...
In worlds so far removed and beautiful than we can ever imagine...

******

"They [Mediums] understand fully that their part in the work being merely passive, the value of the communication in no way exalts their personal merit. It would be foolish to allow oneself to become vain about an intelligent work to which one had only lent mechanical assistance." Allan Kardec's 'The Gospel According To Spiritism.'

Life After Life
What Is The Effect of Knowing That There is no Death?

One of the greatest gifts you can ever give is the release of the fear of death (The Change). With its release comes a wonderful feeling of the enjoyment of this life. Strange, you may think.

Not at all. When that fear has gone and you know that a wonderful 'Afterlife' is there – I put that in quotation marks because the reality is that this existence is just for the blink of an eye in eternity - and what we go to IS the reality, therefore, what we are experiencing, now, is just a 'dream' to experience.

My Guide once said to me of the fear others had of passing: "Why would you be afraid? You were not afraid to be born. You are merely passing back through the door by which you entered."

Once that realisation is in place, wouldn't you want to make the most of this short time? Wouldn't you want to be happier? To make others happy too? If this realisation came then you would also realise that other natural laws would come into play; at least you could look into it couldn't you? Just one example, quite poignant: IF THIS IS TRUE then wouldn't there be some sort of reward, some sort of making up for wrongdoing?

And if that is correct (as it is!) then isn't it better to be kinder? How much better could the world be if we all knew that, while we can all do as we wish, when we have done so much wrong, that we shall all, individually, have to pay for those wrongs? Wouldn't many (not all by any means) think about the consequences? Wouldn't that change the world? So many already know and it wouldn't take much of a percentage to make this world so much better.

2012 was never the "end of the world." It signaled the change that had already started, but increased through 2012 and continued on. There are so many signs that this is happening… just look at places like Syria. Yes, there has been violence but it is in the light of great change by getting rid of dictators; other countries have already done that. There is so much change for the good already in place, how much could our society change?

The world could change radically and it will, it just depends on how quick we can make it happen.

Your light, your power and your kindness can change the world; it will never be perfect because a place of perfection already exists, but we can make it much nearer. As we do so, we recoup (what goes around, comes around). Isn't it better to make a better life for everyone?

Through this book we can show the people of the world, especially the young, who are the future, that we can change our thinking and be good to each other. That we do reap what we sow and that in respect and kindness to all we shall all live together peacefully, spirituality and religion is not always the way to go. The way forward is to be kind and giving to all. To change the culture and give hope to all, especially the young, is the one thing we should all work for...

Leo can be contacted for readings through his website:
www.leo-bonomo.com

Leo's blog:
www.mediumshipandlifeafterdeath.wordpress.com

Leo's Facebook page:
www.facebook.com/Leo.S.Bonomo

Leo is also on blog radio: **www.blogtalkradio.com/live**
It's at 2pm on Tuesdays. Hope you can listen in and contribute too! There will be live readings!

Other books shortly to be published:
'Training for Mediumship – Using the New Energies'.
'A Book of Thoughts – Poems and Thoughts from Spirit'.

Books planned:
'Mr Leslie Flint – Transcripts'. (Leslie Flint was the world's finest Direct Voice Medium)

The Writing Process

The book was written by Automatic Writing, which is spirit thoughts guiding a pen on paper through a Medium.

There are many kinds of trance mediumship. I was given thoughts, pictures and words, until I could resist no more and I would get up from bed. Finding paper and pen, I would go into a trance and when I woke I would read back what had been written. I was reading it for the first time.

The book took three months to write, however, the total time period was approximately three years. Spirit have waited for the right time; this was channelled in 1987.

Those inexperienced may think this remarkable when you consider that often I would have stopped in mid-sentence with sometimes many months in between writing, yet the next trance session began at the very next word.

Apart from spell checking, adding character accents and layout, it is as complete as it was given (with the exception of some of Jimi' Hendrix's lyrics).

As this book has been written by Automatic Writing, I, the Medium, have taken the decision that, as the book was written whole, in trance, with very little interference or colouring, except for accents, spell checks, punctuation etc., that the wiser minds should be left with their work as much intact as possible. There is much that it has taught me in its intact, raw form and this is the reason for its being in the first place after all.

Those of you who are sensitive yourselves will perceive that there are various authors in this work and their flavours are different from each other. You may detect the point when one has taken over from the other. Many people do. Editing will, of course, smooth all of these subtleties out. I feel that, as a work moving on so many spiritual levels, because of the various levels each individual reader is at and with this book being so different, for those reasons, that to edit or over-edit, on this occasion may be wrong. It may transpire in the course of time that this decision is wrong. Should that be so, there will, of course, be an updated version and the differences will be clear.

Therefore, the decision has been taken that to over-edit, or 'tidy up', or otherwise neatly align, as always happens - and properly so with all authors' works - that this has not been done with this work for the reasons stated.

It would be easier (and I dare say more professional) for this to be so, however, the subtle nuances may be lost and as always with things etheric the subtler things sometimes carry the greatest rewards, the more meaning.

With this in mind I ask that you bear with me.

Our thanks go to all involved in the production of this book, both here and in Spirit.

And so the story begins...

Chapter 1

Home Life

Today was a very important day for Alex. The most important day of his young life. The kind of day you only live once. It started the same... but it was to end very differently.

Alex knew that it was different, as sometimes we do. Not straight away... but... something told him. Something deep inside. He wasn't aware of it at first but then... well... it was an idea on the tip of your tongue, one that cannot be brought out... just hanging there... waiting to be spoken. Waiting to be...

It seemed *he knew*... but what was it he knew? There was an expectancy... a comforting that cannot be put into words... it was there... that is it.

Alex was a responsible fourteen-year-old with a good sense of humour. He had a wiry athletic build and short black curly afro hair. His mother was a jolly woman, although her time had had its share of troubles.

His father, as his mother had so often said, had "moved on his way" five years ago and wrote now and then, or as his mother said: "He writes a little, very little."

Alex knew lots of people, but had very few good friends; these friends were all ages and different backgrounds. They were people that were interesting, to him at least.

His gang consisted of nine, two were good mates, Terry and Mel, short for Melvin; others just seemed to be around for having a laugh with.

The 23rd September 1987 was a day like all the rest; it was Wednesday, school days ugh! He got up at eight, same routine. Radio on, heat the milk, fetch the cornflakes, tease the dog.

"School," he thought, "ugh!" As he sat blankly listening to the radio, eating as if on automatic pilot he thought: "Wouldn't it be nice to go somewhere else, fishing maybe". He liked fishing, or the park, but the keeper might report him.

"Are you listening to me?" "Sorry Mum," he said, as she stepped between him and the radio. "If you don't hurry up you'll be late for school, it's twenty-five to nine, now get dressed and hurry up" she said.

"That does it," he thought, "no school for me today." He looked in the mirror, "very tasty," he thought, then poked his tongue out at himself.

In trying to pull his fishing rod out from the shed he only succeeded in tangling himself up with the lawn mower, the hose and his bike. "This will never work," he muttered. "I'm making enough noise to wake the block."

"What on earth are you doing now," his mother cried. "I'm just trying to get my bike out and it's stuck round this stupid hose and everything." "It's no good now," he thought, "I'll have to leave the rod behind or she'll spot it a mile away."

School was a half dozen blocks away and as he mounted his bike he wondered what he might do. At the gate he turned to his mum and stared a long stare. Trance like. "What is it now?" she cried. He hardly heard.

"Goodbye Mum," he said: "Goodbye" and he blew her a little kiss. "Whatever will he do next," she thought. "Goodbye Alex, take care and have a nice day at school." 'School.' The word brought him round.

Alex talked to himself: "School, not that place, not today, I'm going sightseeing, that's where I'm going. I'll turn right instead of left and keep going for a couple of miles just to see where I get. If I get lost I can always ask a policeman," he laughed. "Or maybe not!"

Alex was always interested in people; it was interesting to see the day beginning for other people - shops opening, delivery vans, workman. "Allo gorgeous," he shouted at a young girl in a mock cockney accent. She waved, he blushed and rode on.

Then he came across a pet shop, but not the ordinary kind. It sold reptiles, spiders and such like. "Great, brilliant." He liked anything unusual, something that could catch his imagination. Always got plenty of that, Mum says. There he was in a world of dinosaurs and monsters and beasts a hundred feet tall. A voice interrupted his train of thought: "Shouldn't you be at school?" He looked up at the pet shop man, someone about fifty. "Er...no," he blushed, "I gotta day off."

"Yes, yes and I'm the Duke of Westminster. Now I would appreciate it if you weren't here," he said. "I don't need the police around here". "Why not?" Alex interrupted, "What have you done?" "You cheeky beggar," said the man and chased him up the street.

Alex easily outran him, pushing his bike, laughing all the way up the street. Riding once more, he looked at his watch. 10:30am. "Oh, I've got ages yet," he thought.

In the back of his mind he heard a sound like a car backfire. "Wouldn't it be good if it was a robbery and I was a witness. What would the gang say? I'd be a hero. Cor, what about all the girls? I'd be famous, bet I could be a pop star and me and Mum would live in a big house and..." Suddenly Alex felt himself thrown forward at a pace and he landed in the road. He sat there for a moment and cleared his head.

The driver of the car stuck his head out of the window. It was a big black car and the man looked past Alex dispassionately, looking as though watching a piece of paper that was floating on the wind. Expressionless eyes.

Alex stood up, the car accelerated toward him. "Bleeding idiot," he shouted as he leaped out of the way. The car sped away, tyres screaming round a corner. "Oi! What about my bloody bike?" he said. Shock had got the better of him and by now a small crowd had gathered.

They were huddled in a group beside another a car. "Has someone called the police?" a voice asked. "I think they know, I think they were chasing those thieves." "Don't worry about my bloody bike, will you!" Alex shouted.

"Can someone call an ambulance?" a man called from the crowd. "Don't worry about my bike, will you," Alex shouted at the top of his voice. A police car pulled up and two officers jumped out. "Did anybody see anything?" Sergeant Davis called out. A young woman was crying: "Yes, yes, I saw it all."

"Oh no, not the police, I'll get it now," thought Alex. The police officer walked past him. "Is this the bike?" "Yes," said both Alex and the woman. "And the car came from over there?" he said, pointing. "Yes," said the woman.

He appeared to ignore Alex altogether. "Perhaps he doesn't want me after all," thought Alex hopefully. He managed to manoeuvre his way between the sergeant and a car ducking behind it.

"Right," said the sergeant, scanning the crowd for a reaction. "Who is the boy?" Alex didn't wait any longer. "Oh God, I'd better go," he thought and ran off down the street as fast as he could go. He ran for what seemed like ages.

"Hello," said a voice "...and who are you running from?" Alex stopped and looked around. A head was peeping from behind a corner.

"Sorry?" said Alex. "I bet you are," said the boy. "I'm sorry, I don't understand," said Alex. "I see you're new around here aren't you?" Alex looked around, well it was vaguely familiar but he wasn't sure.

"You were running from someone," said the boy. "Yes," said Alex, blushing. "Well the police won't find you here," said the boy. "By the way I'm Tommy." "I'm Alex," replied Alex. "Where do you live?" asked Alex.

"Oh around, there's a bit of a gang of us and we do mostly what we want and mostly sleep rough and we do have lots of laughs. Do you want to join us?" "Well maybe for a day," said Alex. Tommy laughed very loudly, which made Alex jump.

"Do you always laugh like that?" asked Alex. "Yes," said Tommy sharply with a sneer. Alex suddenly felt very uneasy. "I don't trust you," he thought to himself. Tommy smiled. "Look, we hardly know each other", said Tommy. "Let's be friends and we can have lots of laughs, there's lots of things to do here, come with me." He held his hand out in friendship. Alex didn't take it, he was still uneasy.

They walked on, talking and talking and gradually Alex noticed that the houses seemed to be in poor repair, in fact quite a few were wrecked. It didn't seem to be an area he knew anymore; he had been distracted and now thought he was lost. All of a sudden he could see his mum, she was crying, very hard.

His emotions swelled. "Don't cry Mum," he said. "It will be all right, we'll get through, I'm all right, really I am, it's only a bike after all. I love you Mum, don't worry."

Tommy quickly turned Alex's attention towards a derelict house. "We all used to hang around in there but we've moved on now, more this way," he nodded. "Not too far now." Alex wasn't impressed.

The day was decidedly grey; in fact, as Alex looked, everything seemed grey. For some time now Alex had noticed that they were walking down a shallow slope, which was gradually getting steeper, almost imperceptible at first, though now there was a definite incline.

Alex was getting worried now, the light began to fade. Something worried him. "Not far now," Tommy's voice made him jump. "I think I'll go back," said Alex, "I said, not far now," snarled Tommy. He looked bigger now, menacing. "Yes, menacing is the right word," thought Alex.

Alex found himself running, being chased. Although Tommy was bigger and faster, he never quite caught him. "There was definitely something odd here," thought Alex. Tommy appeared to be enjoying the chase and what he wasn't going to do to Alex when he caught him. Suddenly a sharp stone stung Alex's neck, level with his ear. He cried out and blood greeted his hand.

"I'll get you, you bastard," shouted Tommy. Alex was petrified; people had joined in and wherever he ran he seemed to be going down! The landscape now seemed more like a desert. Now he felt a FEAR like he had never felt before.

Something had happened, something that had threatened his very existence. A large stone caught his shoulder, throwing him off balance, his windmilling arms somehow managed to keep him upright.

Towards a large ditch he ran, with a hoard behind him, crying for his blood. As he looked forward, within a ditch something moved, something evil, he could smell it. It ran towards him at a startling pace. He was cornered and there was no way out.

A huge man came towards him, with matted hair and torn rags for clothes. He had sores and cuts all over him, a long knife in one hand and a half-eaten rat in the other.

Alex's fear GREW and GREW, like a huge wall that was falling on him; they all drew nearer, now closing in, in a circle. "Oh GOD, Jesus Christ help me, dear sweet Jesus, please help me!" His words rang out, clear, ringing like a bell.

Alex awoke and found he was in a bed and a woman was holding his hand. "Oh dear GOD," he said. "Oh dear GOD." The woman spoke to him: "It's all right, it's all right, Alex you're OK. There's nothing to worry about, you'll be all right, you just have to rest for a while, you'll be fine, everything will be explained to you and you'll be fine."

Her soft Irish voice seemed so soothing, so comforting, so kind. "You just rest Alex." He felt himself drifting away. "For a moment there I thought I was dead," he mumbled. "Just take it easy," the words echoed pleasantly around his mind and he went to sleep.

His mum's own uneasy sleep disturbed Alex; her frowning face made him unhappy. She was almost crying in her sleep. "Oh Mum, why are you so unhappy? I'm all right, there's nothing wrong. I love you Mum, I do so love you."

"Poor Mum," he thought to himself, "you don't look well at all. I'm just going to rest and I'll be back with you, to look after you. Don't worry, I'll make you better."

She seemed easier now and he looked around her room at all the little things that signified a women's touch. The trinkets, doilies under small vases, photographs and pictures placed just so and everything neat and tidy. Well, normally so; he noticed that it hadn't been dusted. In fact there were some dirty clothes under the bed. "Poor Mum," he thought. "She must be so tired and... so am I."

Alex went to his room and got into bed. "I'll get up first thing and tidy up and if Mum doesn't wake up too soon, she'll have tea and toast."

Chapter 2

New Arrival

"Good morning Alex." "Morning Mum," he muttered dozily, blinking in the light. "Good morning," said the voice again. As he focused he realised it was the same woman he had spoken to before. "You seem rested," she said. "Yes thank you," said Alex.

He looked around the room, it was similar to a ward. He had been in hospital before, but apart from a few rows of beds and a nurse, the similarity ended.

He shook himself and sat up; the 'ward' had no ceiling! It had no walls! But, it was a 'room' all the same! There was a fantastic blue sky all around and it was nice and warm.

The nurse looked at him. "I think you'll be fine now," she said. "You may get up whenever you want." Alex fell backwards into the bed and put the sheets up over his head. "I think I'm dreaming," he thought to himself. "No, your fine," said the nurse. He sat up again. "I didn't say anything," he said defiantly. "Yes you did, but you didn't speak." He sat there numb. "It's always a bit of a shock at first, well, for a lot of people anyway," she said. Alex wasn't sure what to think; he wasn't sure he dared.

He was just about to say: "Can you read my mind?" when "Yes" interrupted the chain. "Pardon," he said. "Yes, I can read your mind," she started laughing, such an infectious jolly laugh. "It's nothing new here, in fact if you look at my face you will see that I am not talking."

He looked very closely, she was right. "We appear to talk for those who might find it distressing, confusing, or a shock but you, being young, can cope with it far better than someone older, less spiritual or materialistic."

Somehow it didn't appear too strange to Alex. "So I'm reading your mind now?" he said. "Yes," she replied. The realisation that something had happened now dawned on him.

He looked blankly at the nurse, she smiled such a beautiful smile and a great calm came over him. "Yes Alex, you've passed over." It was not a phrase he was used to or had heard before but he knew what it meant.

"When did it happen?" he asked. "Well now," she said. "You would have been here for about four days, although you will find that the measurement of time has no significance here. Once people are used to it, we use the term 'in a space,' such as I'll see you in a space or see you in a while, people meet for an occasion or a purpose."

"When everybody knows the time is right, it's the same when you have to meet someone who is passing over. There is a moment when it is correct; time is only used in connection with the other side."

"Four days! I must have been tired," he thought. "People rest for different reasons Mental and bodily fatigue, disease takes a great toll on the spirit body and it needs to recover." This seemed strange to Alex.

"The period it takes will vary from body to body; mental attitude is so very important. Some people do not believe in this world and therefore completely refuse to acknowledge their surroundings or any help that is offered. If they were extremely wearied when they came over then the period would be longer."

She continued: "Of course, some people do not realise they have passed at all and sometimes it's very like a dream from which they cannot wake up." "And they all end up here," said Alex. "Oh no," she said. "Not by any means, there are several different planes or worlds here, beside the Earth plane and Astral planes and people arrive at the plane that suits them. Mostly they arrive at the sixth plane, the Summerland, which is this one. Each plane has different levels and after spending some time, a space, learning and correcting their faults and purifying themselves, they progress onward, upward. It helps to have a job, something to interest the mind, to concentrate it."

"A job!" thought Alex. "I didn't realise we would have to work." She replied: "You needn't, however you need to rectify your wrongdoings and working for the good of others is one of the best ways," she said.

"Well, it sounds so interesting," thought Alex. "What sort of jobs are there?" "Goodness gracious me," she exclaimed, "I couldn't begin to tell you, there are so many, perhaps you could do this work, or work in the great library." "The what?" he said. "The great library. On most of the planes you will find centres of learning and the great library is one of them. There you will find all kinds of things to learn. There are many centres, or, as we prefer to call them, 'Halls of learning,' as in the bible: 'In my father's house are many mansions.'" Alex look in wonderment "yes, yes, it's all becoming clear, I can see this place is going to be so exciting."

His mind filled with a thousand pictures in an instant, with colours and sounds so beautiful and bright, such hues and notes he never could describe.

"Would you like to go?" He came back with a jolt. "Where?" he wondered. "To one of the festivals," she said. "I'd love to Maria." He was startled by this, he had not consciously asked her name, yet he knew it? It threw him off balance. "Don't worry there are a great many surprises for you here and some will take a little getting used to," she said with a twinkle in her eye. "You have all the time in the world."

Those words hung in the air for ages: "Time in the world, time in the world, all the time, time in the world, all the time, time, time in the world, all the time in the world, in the world, time, time". In the back of his mind a picture began to form; there was something else too.

He waited, then realised it was the ticking of a clock, which, after beginning so faintly, began to get louder. Now the face started to appear. His attention was so taken by these sights and sounds that when they had come sharply into focus he found he was looking directly at a clock tower. Towards the doors he went, where a smell greeted him that was unmistakable. Incense! He thought that through the doors he could hear someone talking and as the sound echoed round, this man was on... "As I stand at this pulpit today, looking at your faces, I hear the question: Does God really care? Does He? Well my brethren, I can tell you that He does care about each and every one of you! God has taken this young boy, yes, but he was given to us for our safekeeping, to feed, to nourish, to teach, the enjoyment he gave to his parents was immeasurable..."

19

Alex looked around, there was AUNTIE FLO! He walked to the front, there was Mum and Dad! His head began to swim. "For this young boy, Alex, whose life was so cruelly taken by the driver of a getaway car, for mere money..." The words faded and Alex looked round at the coffin with its lid tightly shut.

Alex now viewed the gathering from a different point, it was from above and behind the altar. His relatives were listening, some were talking, snide remarks about his parents, words and thoughts were penetrating his brain. "Oh George, you never liked the boy...," "Don't forget we have to go collect that thing, we won't stay long, a few drinks and that's it..."

Some people were laughing, his parents sat together. His mother, he thought, looked quite beautiful. However, there was something opaque about her, almost as if it were a black and white picture. This, he noticed, also applied to his father, who was looking at the coffin. His mother raised her head and looked around the church, her tears wetting her cheek. Their eyes met. A flicker of colour appeared in their hearts and grew from a pinprick of light to a small glow of pinkish mauve. "They love each other again." Alex knew. "Great Father, your world is so beautiful, your gift so great, how can we ever repay you? If only they could see." The black and white had slowly resumed its natural colour; his parents held hands.

"Great Father, your love for us is so great." Alex's emotions swelled; so much joy he felt about to burst, so many thoughts. So many plans, actions, strategies; lines of thought in direct communication with one message behind it all: "God's will be done."

It seemed like a year's work flashed before him in an instant. Hardly able to take it all in, he knew he had made a hundred promises. To who and to what end he did not know, so much to be done, so much to learn. Where would he find the time?

"Time in the world, all in the world, all the time, all the time, time in the world." He found himself with Maria. He felt unable to speak; there was so much to say, where could he start? His emotions swelled so that mere words could not relate.

So many things to do, so many things said, his mind was truly blank. Unable to comprehend what his tasks would be or how he should go about them, he sat for what seemed like ages and slowly his mind perceived a swirling of thoughts that gradually decreased in momentum until at last he jumped up with everything on the tip of his tongue.

He grabbed Maria by the arms and what came out said everything and nothing. "God is so good." He was crying so hard he felt it would stop him breathing; these tears of joy could not, would not, be controlled, it went on for an eternity. He had become touched by love.

"Oh Maria, I have perceived God's work, so wondrous in its beauty, so vast in its plans, so good, so giving, so much love, I have perceived in a moment what would take a lifetime to tell and yet I know what I have perceived is like a grain of sand compared to all the known universes."

He talked for ages, so excited and yet frustrated that the formulation of an idea that cannot be described is now known. He compared it to telling the complete historical and technological times of the Earth from its beginning, giving in detail every aspect of all the sights and attitudes. "That would be a real shaker for Mastermind, wouldn't it now!" he laughed. Becoming more serious he said: "and yet it all seems so simple." "Ah yes," Maria interjected, "the mind works much quicker here, but you have received instructions from a higher soul. These plans will be carried out when they are due."

"My mentor did not give his name, but I feel he's two planes further up," said Alex, hoping for confirmation. "You will meet at the correct occasion, do not struggle with his identity, he will make himself known," she said.

"I found myself *at the funeral,*" he said. He avoided saying "my." "My" seemed a very strange word to say. "Oh yes, lots of people experience that" said Maria. "Those who are very materialistic very often stay with the body, others are drawn into the grave itself, wherever it might be, to view the body decomposing at various stages. Sometimes it's because these persons have fixed ideas of death and believe that when you are gone you are put in a hole and left, therefore they feel that's where they should be."

21

"I see," said Alex "at the funeral they said I'd passed over after being run down, that can't possibly be right, you see when I was being chased by Tommy..." his thoughts ran off and his mind fumbled for an answer.

"Alex, I think your work may involve helping people who have difficulty passing. Your experience of passing shows you that it is all too easy to miss what has happened; people's experiences vary greatly. However, quite a few like yourself do not realise that they have made the change, especially if it has to be sudden." He pondered for a moment, "What about Tommy?" he asked, "He knows full well he has passed, but he occupies the lower planes, they will not help you" said Maria.

"They are envious, greedy and evil souls who are attracted to your light. They wish you harm. They are enmeshed in a world of self-pity and atrocious acts, their actions fed by burning desires to bring souls down to their own level. It is what they call 'hell,' on the Earth plane any way. To relieve these souls of their torture requires great patience. It is serious minded work, undertaken only by those strong enough to do so. Some of these souls would be there forty or fifty of your Earth years, some a hundred, others more.

"These souls are fully entrenched in their deeds, delighting in the torture and brutalisation of others. Since the ones being victimised cannot 'die,' their time seems endless. However, if they escaped they would only torture another, only too happy to inflict what they had received. Freedom is attained when a flicker of light, or God's love, or realisation that things need not be that way is reached. The flame is kindled by the higher souls until they are ready to progress onward, upward.

"Of course there are many degrees on each plane; when you are ready you will see, but for now you must take things slowly, get used to the place again."

"Again?" thought Alex. "Why yes," said Maria, "during your sleep state you may have had cause to visit the Spirit World and you would most certainly have lived before."

Alex thought about this for a while. "Of course," he said, "it's all so clear, you really can't expect anything else when you view it from our angle." "Quite," said Maria softly.

"How long have you been here?" he asked. "Oh, for some time, I can't say precisely," she said, "I still have a long way to go and so much to do. I enjoy my work, it's very rewarding, there is so much to learn and do in whatever field you follow or have an interest in, then there are the theatres and plays." He sat in amazement. "Theatres? Plays?"

"Yes, they are very popular, they are mainly historical, with real characters playing themselves. Of course, they may differ from the normal history books you may have read, either because the facts have been blurred, or due to propaganda techniques. Later we will go and have a look round, OK?" "Great, brilliant," Alex was now excited at the prospect of being able to discover many things. He began to think of all the things he had an interest in, lots of them. Dinosaurs! He smiled.

He lay down and thought things just seemed so natural and right; everything just right. Perfect. He drifted off again, this time he knew he was resting. His body looked like a tube, which slowly filled with a pinkish light; its sensation was similar to a sort of heat, in a pleasant form, with a tingle in all the places which were tense, wearied, or not well. This feeling continued for a short while. When this lightened feeling faded, Alex noted that his normal white light appeared brighter and he felt fitter and better than ever before. He thought: "I feel so good and Mum is so sad." Within an instant he found himself at her bedside and she appeared to wake. "Alex," she said. "My darling Alex." "Mum, I'm fine, I feel really well, there is such happiness here, everything is fine, it's all OK." She replied: "Thank God Alex."

"Do not worry Mum, I love you now as I always have done and will look after you, there is nothing to fear or worry about, God bless you, keep you always in His sight." At his words she seemed to look and feel better.

"Better..." the thought struck him. "I wonder?" He focused his mind on her until her body filled with a pinkish light, which changed to a slight light green and however hard he tried it would not go pink. Behind him, Alex was aware of some friends and helpers. He gathered their thoughts of good intention and realising they knew better, watched and took in all that went on. No matter how he tried their identities remained hidden, but knowing God's love guided all, he was content to let them leave when their work was completed.

Maria stood before him. "I see you are learning fast and have been giving your mother healing then." "Yes," he said. "When your mother wakes in the morning she will think she has had a dream about you, but she will know it's not a dream, she will know you are safe." "People often dream of their loved ones after death, don't they?" he said. "Yes," she replied, "their loved ones let them know they are all right. If they are fairly well it usually takes a week or so, but it will always vary, as you know, though this is not always the case, as some people do not choose to come through."

Alex and Maria found themselves in a beautiful green field with a brook. The grass was so soft it could have been fluffy downy feathers; the water looked so cool and inviting. "You may go in," said Maria and without a second thought he was in waist deep, the water cleansing his very soul. It felt brilliant, it was clear, so refreshing and tasted so very good. "Oh Maria, this is fantastic." He climbed out. In the distance he could see a dome. It belonged to a small building that had been placed in another field, some distance away. "That," said Maria, "is a building that has several purposes, meditation, instruction and refinement being three of them. It is called by some 'The Temple of Truth.' Go forward and we shall see."

Within one or two steps Alex found himself outside the building, the symmetry and excellence of workmanship astounded him. It appeared to be made of bright white light translucent stone. Everything about it was perfect. It was, he estimated, about twenty foot high and perhaps fifteen foot wide. Alex walked round it, looking in wonderment: "God's work is beautiful." "It certainly is," replied Maria, "watch." A man appeared and walked towards the temple, oblivious to the fact that Alex and Maria were there, up some stone steps to a door which opened by itself and closed behind him. He sat for a moment, crossed legged in the centre of the floor. It was in a sense quite plain inside but still very beautiful. Alex could see he was uneasy. When he had calmed, a pure white light filled the dome through a 'tube' of light from the heavens. It proceeded to cleanse the man. This done, it stopped 'filling' the building but maintained cleansing the man. The dome filled with pictures and thoughts, voices and sounds were heard. "Is it a cinema?" asked Alex sheepishly. Maria turned sternly toward him. "It most certainly is not," she said firmly. She need not have said anything, Alex already knew.

The man began weeping; as well as pictures and sound within the dome, there was emotion. "What's being relayed back to the man were his past indiscretions, bad thoughts, acts of selfishness, actions and inactions. It is no good performing a kindness, whilst thinking ill of someone." Maria's words shook Alex; it seemed as if she knew all about him. It is common on the Earth plane to say that in near death experience your life flashes before your eyes; however, it is nearer the truth than many would like to know. It is one of the realisations that come as a surprise when you arrive here. The mind is God's camera; it does its work well. Every action, thought and feeling is remembered; nothing, but nothing, is un-recalled.

"All actions, for good or bad, are recalled to be used for your betterment. It's no good living the apparent life of a saint whilst thinking bad things. What's most important are the reasons and thoughts behind the actions. Doing charity work because you think people will love you for it is wrong. Doing it because you love people is what counts. For each bad or unproductive thought and action you must make amends; however this is not the end, for every action good or bad provides a reaction, this is the law, God's law and it is the Law of Cause and Effect. Your actions affect others, who in turn, rightly or wrongly, base their actions on yours. It is a ripple effect - the Law of Cause and Effect. You will learn much about Cause and Effect and how these ripples go forward through time and space. One good or bad thought can have such momentum, it is awe-inspiring.

"This man is beginning to realise the errors of his ways and how much good he has done; bad thought precipitates bad thought, as does good. For the bad he has done he must work for the good of others, for every wrong done to him he must learn to forgive. The murdered must forgive the murderer. Once we all truly love one another we shall begin to know God's love. Each man must face himself. It is the will of God, for only then can we truly progress."

"Is this a bad man?" asked Alex. "Those who are truly evil or bad inhabit the lower planes," said Maria "the realisation of his actions and thoughts have come home to him, good and bad. These tears are also tears of joy, for his goodness he will be rewarded."

"So the evil ones will have to work themselves from the lower planes and then onto here?" said Alex. "Just so," replied Maria. "Will I have to visit this place?" said Alex. "Of course, but only when the time is right." "Why can't we be seen?" he asked. "We are hidden from his perception only for your benefit," she replied. "Mine?" he asked. "Yes, have you not learned from this?"

He thought for a while and realised he had. Before he could ask another question Maria interjected: "And do you think this lesson has benefited you?" Thinking harder and clearer now, he realised that thoughts and actions took on a different meaning.

"It is viewed at a different angle on Earth," he said. "An incorrect angle, all our experiences at what we would judge to be good or bad are basically experiences on which the soul learns. At every turn God's love gives us a decision to do the right or wrong thing. The right thing is not always the thing that, as a human, we would wish for, in fact it may cause us great discomfort and pain. If the decision is taken on selfish grounds, the loss to the soul is twofold. Firstly, the actions and reactions take their path, secondly, the selfish thought draws the soul down further, envelopes it. If the correct decision is made, the gain to the soul is immense firstly; the actions and reactions take their path secondly; the thought raises the soul's vibration and takes it higher thirdly; the discomfort, pain or inconvenience to which the soul is possibly subjected to by its decision will be rewarded a hundred fold.

"As like attracts like, the soul will attract good souls, who in turn will help and shower God's love upon that soul, which, being happy at its decision, will help to uplift its own vibrations even more. Fourthly, being willing to help others will lead to further situations where its chance to help will be required, which will accelerate the process even further.

"The reason God gives us the right to make our own decisions is because of His great love and understanding. Jesus could appear on Earth now and make everyone know who he is, but that would take away people's free will decisions. If a naughty boy is told not to do something and thinks he cannot be seen, he will do as he pleases. A father will teach his children that a fire is hot but it is only after a child is burned that he realises the meaning of hot, but the child will have learnt from the experience.

"If a man is left to his own devices, only then will we see the true being. If a man believes this is his only life and there is no reparation for his misdeeds, he will then act as he sees fit as 'a naughty child hidden from view,' an enlightened being from whom the truth is withheld will also act as he sees fit, however their good intentions are markedly different. To learn, the soul must experience, to know the difficulties. You could liken it to driving a car," he explained. "It all looks very easy, especially with an experienced driver, however; as every learner knows, the difficulties of co-ordination and use are many.

"It's the same with incarnation. It is easier to judge mistakes with the benefits of the particular view we have. It is easier to view with dismay the addiction of a drunk. However, Karmic forces may dictate that the lesson for you to learn at this time is how easy it is to be submissive to alcohol. Think how easy it is to merely move and yet it takes a child a time to master even its first steps, to use the body for its purpose; to command it to obey is no easy thing and yet the difficulties encountered are, in truth, minute. The incarnation brings with it a lesson and therefore an appreciation of the difficulties involved; each successive life purifies us and teaches us that until the time when we are purest, we can at last come closer to the Great Father."

For a moment Alex stood stunned. He looked blankly at Maria as the last words echoed round his mind. "Did I just say all that?" "Yes," she replied. "It didn't sound like me, in fact I was listening as hard as you were and yet I was talking so naturally, but at the same time it was strange."

"Alex," she said, "you are an old soul, an experienced one and you will find circumstances will bring that experience back to you. You have important work to do; your work will be greatly appreciated by those who you can help."

"I spoke of walking, but it only seemed a few steps from the brook to the dome, yet it seemed a fair way?" "Well yes," she said, "we can walk if we want to, but in reality we only need to think of a place to get there. It's a bit like flying but much quicker, instantaneous. This is what gives rise to the ideas of Angels and wings. It was the easiest way to communicate the theory to people." "What if I didn't know where a place was, but I thought about it, what would happen?" asked Alex. "Well, it is possible that it does exist here on this plane or lower. In that case you would find yourself there. If you were imagining a place, you would know if it were not real and would act accordingly. If you believed a place to be real, it would be a very different. Let me show you," she said.

Alex found that they were on a small path. They walked slowly up, Alex noticing that they were actually walking up, with each step higher in the air. "This is amazing, brilliant," he said. She turned her face towards him and put a finger to her lips, signifying him to be silent.

They walked awhile towards some clouds. Soon they were immersed in some cool, damp clouds and within a few steps came to a clearing. Alex stood dumb-founded. There was a young man, playing a harp, singing and there on his back were a huge pair of white wings!

"I just don't believe it?," he whispered. "Oh yes," said Maria "there is the crux of the matter. Timothy does believe it... his idea of heaven is just what you see. It is an idea so fixed in his mind that he has been here a while, yet he is progressing; every now and then he wonders why it is so unchanging. His guides and helpers are coaxing him gently; those things cannot be rushed."

"But it all seems so real. I can see, feel and hear all that is happening. If it were a house it would be solid to the touch," said Alex. "Just so," she said. "However, it is all created by his mind. What you can see and feel are his thoughts. Those thoughts have created this world - to him it is real. He is trapped by his own limitations, by his failure to diagnose what is happening to him. He has a fixed idea and a stubborn mind. It is these that are holding him back."

Alex spoke up: "If he had knowledge of the Spirit World, would he have known what to expect?" "It would certainly have helped," replied Maria. "His mind would have been open to more positive suggestions and he would have been better off."

Compassion began to swell in Alex's heart. "Has he been here long?" he asked sadly. "You have already asked," said Maria, hinting the thought had already been picked up. "But it has been around five Earth years."

This shocked Alex. Five years... five years here? He looked around. Five years in this space! "Can we do anything to help him?" he asked. "Yes, is the short answer, but it can only be when the time is right," "Oh when will that be?" he said sadly. "God knows," said Maria softly with a knowing look in her eyes, her smile was so sweet.

Alex found himself being lowered down. The movement was slow and firm. He was getting used to odd feelings of movement. Now he could feel his concentration much sharper and now the clouds felt really cold and clammy. He walked forward to a clear path and he realised he was carrying something. It was a harp.

"Hello," said a voice, "it's nice to see you." It was Timothy. Alex scoured round for sight of Maria - there was none. "You don't see many people here," said Timothy. He put one hand to the side of his face. "I think they're all down below," he whispered with a wink.

"I'm Timothy," he said. "I... I'm Alex," said Alex, a little shaken. "Very nice to meet you." They shook hands. "Don't you get bored here?" asked Alex. "No," replied Timothy. "Well...perhaps a tiny bit but I can always play my harp," he said cheerfully.

"Dear me," thought Alex, "I'd be bored stiff!" "Did you say something?" asked Timothy. "No," said Alex. "He obviously hasn't got the hang of it yet," thought Alex. "I'm sorry," said Timothy, thinking he had heard something again. "That's all right," said Alex ignoring the questions.

"What else do you do?" "Well I sweep the clouds and I sing." "Oh yes, I heard," thought Alex. "Pardon?" said Timothy, who by now was getting confused as Alex's lips had once again not moved. "I'm sorry," said Alex, apologising and now realising his mistake. "What for?" asked Timothy, who by now was getting a little agitated.

"Did you say other people came here?" asked Alex, changing the subject. "Yes, one or two, I couldn't see them clearly, I think they were too far away" "Don't you find it clammy and cold here?" asked Alex.

Timothy was just about to "No" when he thought about it. "Well, just a bit," he said. Alex could see it was something of a revelation. "I find it very damp, I expect it could go through to your bones after a while." Timothy was beginning to agree. "Look," said Alex, "why don't we go somewhere where it's warm?"

Timothy was startled, his lips went dry and his eyes were wide open. He swallowed a lump. "You don't mean down there?" he said, pointing to below his feet. Alex knew now that this was not going to be easy. "No, no, nowhere near *there*, just somewhere sunny" Timothy paled. He never thought the devil would come up here for him. "Sunny," he murmured. "Warm."

"If he weren't dead already, I swear rigor mortis had set in," thought Alex. "Pardon?" said Timothy limply. "If we go *up* this way," said Alex, pointing, "it's a bit warmer." Alex emphasised the up again. "Up?" murmured Timothy. "Up," echoed Alex.

The colour began to return to Timothy's cheeks. "Up?" he said again. "Yes, *up*, this way," said Alex, pointing. Alex held out his hand and pointed with the other. "This way," he said. Shaking, Timothy took his hand and together they walked. Gradually the clouds thinned out and they found themselves on a grassy mountain track, with the warm and ever-blue sky radiating down.

Timothy looked out over the fields and trees. "This is so beautiful," he said, "so very beautiful." "Better than clammy old clouds ay," said Alex. "Oh yes, this is...is heaven," Timothy said. "Yes, I suppose it is," said Alex, although he thought of his divine inspiration and the promises he had made. His tiny peek at the next plane, which was as far as removed from this beauty as heaven was from hell. "What a strange way to put it," he thought, "but somehow very apt."

"There is so much to see and do here..." Alex began. "But first Timothy must rest," the familiar voice of Maria sounded once again. "Timothy," said Alex, "this is my good friend Maria and she will take care of you." "Yes," said Maria, smiling a knowing smile at

Alex. His mind became impressed with the words, "Well done Alex. Your first task is over."

They found themselves back at the ward, Alex excitedly telling Timothy about the things that he discovered. Together they made this plan and that. Timothy explained to Alex the feeling of his position in *heaven*: "It's just what you expected, well, what I expected anyway. It seemed so right, nothing was out of place, I hadn't a hint of any wrong. OK, I didn't see many people; I just assumed we were all too busy; obviously, not everyone gets to heaven do they? So it seemed right that there were not too many around. It was so very natural, so very real." Alex agreed: "I was so surprised by its reality, the feel, it's almost as if I'd walked on to a film set, from one stage onto another."

"Well," said Maria, "It was real. Thought waves are very powerful, that's how the buildings here are created." "But the wards don't have walls Maria?" said Alex. "Ah, but that's for a purpose, everything here is perfect and everything has a reason and its meaning will be known when you are able to take it in."

"If you don't mind," said Timothy, "I think I'll sleep now, I feel very tired." He walked to a bed and lay down. Maria beckoned to Alex and he walked toward her. "Come this way," she said. Within a few steps they were walking down a corridor. From the look and smell Alex knew it was a hospital. "This is strange," he thought, but he wasn't sure why. They walked past a desk and turned left into casualty, the ward seemed compact and personal, while giving the impression of space. Everything appeared normal. Across the room, through some swing doors, came a nurse leading a woman of around forty-five, who appeared to be in a state of shock. "There, there," said the nurse, "you will be fine, you're just shaken up, you sit down there and we will check you over. Would you like a cup of tea?" "Yes?" The woman nodded. "OK love, we will soon have you right as rain." The woman was led to a small cubicle and given tea while the nurse carried on checking her. "What's your name, love?" she asked. "Catherine," came the reply, "I'm just so lucky to be alive. I don't know what happened, the car just lost control, I skidded and bounced off the crash barrier and..." She broke off, sobbing. "It's all right Catherine, just take it easy you will be just fine, do you want

31

another cup of tea?" Catherine nodded. "Sister Maria will you get her another?" Maria stepped forward with the tea. Alex stood open-mouthed in wonderment; to him it was as if he were in a Disney film where cartoon characters just stepped into real life. He tried grasping the concept and then realised how silly he was being.

This was not a real Earth hospital! It was a Spirit one! Catherine had, of course, passed over but as she was unable to comprehend all that had happened, she was being treated, as she would expect to be treated, by nurses in a hospital. Taking details, a police officer came through the swing doors and spoke to one of the nurses and walked over to Catherine and the Sister. "Are you all right Madam?" he asked. She nodded thankfully. "Well now, you have made a bit of a mess of the car, haven't you? Never mind, nobody is hurt, that is the main thing. I understand they are going to keep you in for observation and give you something to make you sleep. I'll be back a bit later and take a statement and a few details and will see you then."

"It wasn't my fault," she blurted out and began to cry, "I just don't know what happened, it's not my fault." The policeman spoke gently to her: "Nobody said it was, did they?" His kindly face reassured her. "We just need details... for our records, you understand?" He patted her hand gently. "You've had a big shock and you need to rest." "She'll be fine with us Constable," said Sister. He turned and went. "Isn't the process wonderful?" said Alex to Maria. "Of course," she said with a smile, "just perfect."

Alex looked into another cubicle and got a shock for there was somebody lying on a stretcher in a very sorry state, with blood-soaked bandages around his legs. "This one's a thief," said Maria telepathically. "He fell off a wall through a glass roof and cut himself badly and couldn't, therefore, walk, in fact," she said looking at Alex, "they haven't found him yet."

Alex took her meaning, immediately he started to say: "When," but was interrupted by Maria's thoughts. "Four hours, thirty-five minuets," she smiled. "He slipped at eleven fifty-five and will be found at seven forty-six; however, the times are quite irrelevant. He has these bandages because he knows he is hurt and expects to have them; he is experiencing some pain even though he

32

has been anaesthetised. However, this will be taken from him shortly. He feels the pain because he expects to; his experiences of being badly hurt before tell him he is bound to be uncomfortable even with painkillers."

"It just seems as though everything is thought out, every detail fits," Alex said "Well, you see," said Maria, "all the details are in your mind, up here." She tapped her temple with her index finger: "All our experiences, everything." She turned to Alex: "Even the snag in your sweater." For a moment he was shaken, then he followed her gaze to a spot near to his ribs and sure enough a tiny thread had been pulled out and caused a run which spread a couple of inches towards his tummy. "I never knew this was here," he said. "No, not consciously perhaps, but it is a detail of your dress that has been recreated by your mind, which has neither added nor taken way any detail, but simply organised your thought patterns into something that is useful or needed by you, or something which is comforting or familiar," said Maria.

"Can anything be recreated by thought?" he asked. "Yes," came the reply, "but only if it is of service and benefit to you; there is no need to wear clothes here," she said. Alex blushed at the thought. "We do for modesty's sake, but of course people normally wear clothes so we do," she said.

"Is this building made of thought?" asked Alex. "Yes," came Maria's reply. "However, its creator has a more powerful mind than ours. We could not change its structure." "Oh, I was wondering about that" said Alex. Maria interjected: "Shortly, we shall visit one of the halls of learning, there are books on all subjects and you can read to your heart's content." "It must be a real big place!" he said in wonderment. "I think the word 'huge' is vastly insufficient," conjectured Maria. "You will find a copy of every Earth book ever written except, of course, the naughty ones." A slight smile crossed her lips. "In addition to this are the vast amounts of Spirit-only books and papers, which are very interesting."

"You mention that the boy who is a thief will be found at seven forty-six," said Alex. "Precisely," added Maria. "How do you know?" he asked. "I presume that the time is in advance of this moment?" She replied, "Quite correct, in fact we will travel to that spot for there is something for you to see. But going back to your question, you must understand that everything is known in the Spirit World. All things past, present and future. However, we are only informed at the precise moment we need to know, so that the information may be used for benefit; sometimes it is passed on in the form of dreams or premonitions, or to mediums or people with second sight."

"I thought mediums and gypsy fortune tellers were all fakers?" said Alex. "No, no, my dear, far from it," said Maria, "although there are many who profess to know and some who add or enlarge on what little information they receive. These people will reap a huge amount of sorrow for themselves; it is done mainly for greed. There are many fine mediums around, in all manner of cultures, who offer genuine help to those who seek it. However, it is sometimes a bitter pill to swallow, for answers wanted are not always those given. People do not realise the meaning of suffering or why a certain phase of hardship must be endured. Some of these people only want to know when they will win the lottery, when will they be lucky in love. Those who seek material things will find materialists to take money from them and tell them things they want to hear.

"True mediumship is a gift to let people know that God does exist, or at least an all powerful force exists. It shows people that there is no need to fear death, which is simply a phase of changing one experience or existence for another. It shows that if you do truly love thy neighbour you will be rewarded, that good really does triumph over evil. Good is always portrayed on Earth as white or light colours and evil as black or dark; once you become used to it you will see the auras around people and feel the person's character and feelings. Persons of high spiritual nature and goodness have a light and bright aura. Those who do not have this nature have dark auras and some can appear black."

"Great Father!" cried Alex with great emotion. "Dear God!" "Whatever is wrong?" asked Maria. Alex shuddered at the memories, even now he felt faint, he fell to his knees and began to cry. "Please tell me Alex?" she asked. "Please tell me about it."

"When I was ten," he began, "on a warm night a strange experience befell me, which although I knew was not a dream could

34

only recount as one until now, the horror and feelings of which I have never, ever forgotten and now never will. The true horror of this experience had not struck home until you spoke and now I know it to be true." Alex began to recall the experience. Subconsciously he began to build up the thought forms, which intensified as the memories came back. "I was asleep, I had been dreaming," he seemed to be checking every word, "but then a different stage emerged, I found myself flying, although I knew where I was going," his eyes were beginning to open in wonder. "It seemed peaceful somehow; I looked down on the ramparts of a castle, built of grey stone. Being interested, I found myself going down toward it and I landed on these ramparts, where there were some steps. The height was great so I ventured down the steps my curiosity running wild. It led to a great corridor which ran the length of this wall, some eighty feet, with what appeared to be a single door near the end. The castle now appeared to be cold, murky and damp. I took a few hesitant steps along and became aware of something approaching the ramparts at great speed. A shiver ran along my spine, I wanted to turn back. My legs were frozen with fear."

Alex's face grew white as he seemed almost to be shaking with fright at the memory of it. His eyes were wide and filling with tears. "It landed. Its presence sucked out the light. Its putrid smell choking yet shocking my body into action. My legs seemed to move in slow motion, while my heart and mind raced. Every movement an effort, with a hundred thoughts in between. It followed mockingly, sensing my suffering and feeding upon it like a cannibal, a vampire. It made no noise, it played its game. Now I had reached the door, the terrified cry of a tortured soul still frozen in my throat. If I could have smashed this door open, even with my head, I would have tried. I tore and scratched at it until I realised I had not, in my blind panic, tried the handle. Behind me the evil things breath was hot and its evil personality formed a smothering black cloak, which had dense form. The handle turned slowly and the huge door grunted on its hinges, trying to resist my push whilst slowly moving. Through the door, I glanced over my shoulder as I threw my weight to close it; this monster, which felt so near, was still twenty foot away! It had no form, just a black shadow of evil. As the door closed, I threw the bolts. Any sighs of relief I may have had were quashed by the stunning disbelief that its personality, so evil and strong, preceded it by some sort of projection. Suddenly I felt myself being physically pushed from the door by this evil thing.

"I wished and hoped that I could explode into a million pieces so it would never find me. I looked around; there was only a small window! I poked my head through and several hundred feet below lay the ground. Such a fear of heights touched me that momentarily I stepped back. The door was open! The room began to darken, pitch black from the doorway where it entered! I knew that even death would not keep me safe. It would devour my very soul. Even though the word death petrified me, I gladly welcomed it and launched myself out the window as the very light itself was snuffed out within the room. On the way down to the ground I could have cried a million tears of joy, however, there was little chance of that.

"The thing had followed and it was travelling faster than I was! And its presence was stronger than ever. When I was about to hit the ground I woke. My heart was physically hurting my chest with each beat. My left arm was numb and tingling. My body and bed were both covered in cold sweat and I was breathing as though I had just run ten miles. I almost choked, my death cry stifled in my throat. It took me fully half an hour to recover and dry myself. Finally, convincing myself it was a nightmare, I began to settle down. As my eyes began to close, I was dragged to sleep again. In a second I was being chased, with this howling insane laughter following me, I jumped up, my chest pounding, my brow in sweat. Three more times I tried to sleep and three more times it tried to destroy me. In the end I decided no more sleep for me. I believe the experience brought on a mild heart attack. If I had died there and then I believe I would have had no existence in any way, shape or form."

Maria listened intently to all that was said. When he had finished she spoke slowly: "It's a terrible tale and unfortunately it's true. You had visited the lower planes and met with one of the inhabitants, which, as terrible as it was, was not the worst."

"Great Father!" he exclaimed. "Not the worst!" "No, not by a long chalk," said Maria. "You see, you said it was all grey, but there are regions where it is black! So dark you cannot see your hand in front of your face!" His heart felt heavy; there was a feeling of depression he had never known. "These poor, poor people. However did they come to this?" "Ah yes, poor souls indeed, but do not trouble yourself with these thoughts, you have enough time for work." This last comment puzzled Alex but he let it go.

Maria cocked her head to one side, as though listening to a faint sound. "We must go now," she said, smiling sweetly, "to see the boy." She took his hand and together they walked forward. To Alex the journey appeared more of a struggle than when he went to the church. The air somehow felt 'thicker.' It was difficult to explain. Maria understood: "Well, technically our bodies are of much finer, higher vibration than it is on Earth. The vibrations there are denser, so it feels we are struggling against it. You also have got used to your finer body. When you first pass over you are still very close to Earth and still accustomed to its density. But, of course, you do get used to your new body fairly quickly..." "Depending," said Alex interrupting, "on your spiritual nature, materialistic views and how long you take to recover." "Quite," she said. They both laughed.

Before them appeared an outline of a building. Its blurred and distant form came slowly into focus and then Alex realised it was the building that housed the body of the young man. Once inside, he turned his attention smartly to the clock, it read seven forty-one. Behind some large cabinets, which formed a partition, lay the body. Looking upwards he saw the shattered roof; unexpectedly, he found himself at eye level with the remaining glass, as the thought of "glass" entered his mind.

Looking around, he could see the rooftops and down below was the body, the face contorted in pain, deathly white. Alex found himself close to the body. Showers of glass had cut the thigh to pieces. "This one did most of the damage." Alex jumped, it was Maria. She pointed to a large piece sticking out from the right leg. "Of course, the shock helped." Alex looked at the blood. "There's a lot of it," he exclaimed, "I suppose there is," agreed Maria.

Alex checked the clock. It read seven forty-one. The puzzlement in his mind had not formed into words when Maria had said: "No, it hadn't stopped, we are just moving too fast. Our minds work much faster than when in the body and as we only need to think of a place to go there, you have just surveyed the scene very quickly, in Earth terms at least."

A sound startled Alex. It was a key turning in a lock. His first reaction made him want to hide. "I can't see any point in that," he said to Maria with a smile. "Neither can I," she replied. The sound came from three rooms away and an old man had entered and put a bunch of keys on a bench and closed the door.

"Right, first things first," he said loudly to himself. He slapped his hands and rubbed them together. "A nice cup of Rosie, got to get yer priorities right old son."

Alex laughed. He remembered occasions when he had talked to himself in the same way. "Everybody does it," said Maria interrupting his thoughts.

"That's it, kettle on, now for a Tom Tit and I'll be able to face the day." He passed through two doors that separated an office and disappeared through another. "Effing bastards," shouted the man. "This is it," thought Alex, "here we go." "Can't these stupid bastards find anything else to do? Fancy throwing all the bog paper in the pan I'll have to wait now until the shops open. You wait until they come in, I'll tell them." He fumed around, throwing sugar in a mug along with a tea bag. "Perhaps Harry's got some bog paper in his locker?" he said aloud. He walked back through the office, past the toilet, down a short corridor and left through another to the large cabinets. He tried Harry's door. "Damn an' blast, locked. Tell you what ol' son, its bloody cold in here, we'll av' to be having the fire on." He said this loudly. This made Alex think of his own actions when alone. "Funny, isn't it?" he mused.

The man's gaze turned upwards, "No bloody wonder," he said. "No bloody wonder." He walked behind the cabinets to a sight that shook him. He didn't like the look of blood at the best of times, but this made him feel sick. Alex looked for the clock. It read seven forty-six precisely. He looked at Maria, who was totally unimpressed by the timing and who had been studying both Alex and the man intently. The man was absolutely shocked by his find. So shocked that all he could say every now and again was: "Oh shit." The piercing scream of the kettle brought him round. It had almost boiled dry.

"I suppose I'd better call the police and an ambulance, even though the poor sod's past help," he thought.

The man still looked dazed as he poured water into the mug. He cradled it in his hands as he sat shivering. Alex watched the scene with an intense feeling of concentration; every detail committed to memory, every action and reaction and thought, both the man's and his own. Suddenly the man jumped up and ran back to the scene where the realisation that it wasn't a dream turned to panic. He knelt beside the body and pounded on its chest, crying heavily: "You stupid effing bastard, why me? Why me? Why didn't you die somewhere else? Why? Just for money, just for the effing money."

He sat there for a few seconds. With the tension released he felt a little better. "Christ!" he suddenly remembered. "I'd better get the police and ambulance."

"That's right Officer, an attempted break in and a death," there was a pause as he listened to the answer, "Well, no not yet, I'll call right away." He replaced the receiver and immediately called the owner. He sat down to fill his mug again. A sharp knock startled him some time later. "Open up, it's the Police." He shuffled to the door. "All right, all right I'm coming." He pulled the door back. "Come in, cup of Rosie?" "Actually, we'd like to see the body... *if* it's all right with you?" said the Officer. "Oh that? That's through there," he said pointing with his hand, "just follow thro'."

A second Officer followed through while a third asked him if he was all right. "Can be a bit of a shock, especially if it's messy." "Oh, it doesn't bother me," said the man, "seen worse in the war." "Yes, expect so," said the Officer with a smile. "Still, you do look a bit pale." The man looked sharply at the Officer, hoping his stare would not be matched. Thankfully the kettle boiled and he turned away. "Natural colour init."

Maria interrupted the proceedings: "Bravado, a dangerous thing, caused the death of many." Alex paused and thought of the times that he and his friends played a game of 'dare.' Stupid, really stupid. A boy from his school was killed running across a railway track, just for dares. Just for bravado. "We must go now," Maria said and took his hand.

Chapter 3

Library

"It's so beautiful," said Alex, "so calm, so good." "Yes" replied Maria; her concentration was not with him. He turned to see someone lying in a bed in the ward.

All around was a strong blue light, very pale and such a hue that he'd never seen before, almost an electric blue. "She seems to be asleep," he whispered. "It's OK," said Maria, "she can't hear you, she's resting.

"She has been ill for some time, for years with cancer and she needs a lot of rest. Little by little it ate away at her until it invaded most parts of her body but," she said pointedly, "she was a brave soul, did not complain and did her best for others until the end, even though she was in great pain."

"When I slept, was I being healed too?" asked Alex. "To a minor extent," she said, "you only needed rest, you were young and healthy and passed quickly."

"Ah yes," he said and thought of Mum. He visualised she was in the kitchen washing up; she was thinking of him too. "God bless you Alex, keep you always safe."

Her thoughts reached up to him and filled him with joy, like a physical touch. He reached out to the vision and touched her shoulder... she felt it!!! She felt it!

His emotions swelled and he cried tears of happiness. "Oh Maria, isn't it so wonderful? His work is so good, to actually make your presence known in this way it's...it's...brilliant." Words had almost failed him.

He rested for a while and then he looked around, out over the fields, with the warm air around him and took in all the details one by one until in the distance he saw something he could not quite make out. Concentrating he focused his mind upon it and slowly it came into view.

"A building! A beautiful building and more." As he focused, several buildings came into view. "A town! A town!" he exclaimed excitedly, "A town!" He scanned the buildings and read in carved letters on the front of one of them 'LIBRARY.'

"Oh God, it's there, the great library, it's there!" Before he could repeat himself again he found it was here, not there. In fact, he was on the steps facing the main doors. He turned to see groups of people chatting; some sitting, some standing, some playing.

This building shone. It was the only way he could describe it, it actually shone. It seemed to be made of something similar to Mother of Pearl, but it glowed in a very pleasing way. There was an energy that surrounded it; mostly it was a sense of love but other things too. He wasn't sure what, but it was beautiful.

"Just like a university, I suppose," he thought to himself. "Similar," said a voice behind him. He turned to see a slightly built girl. "Are you new here?" she said.

"Well er... fairly," he replied, "I've just not been here," he said, pointing down with his finger.

"Oh I guess you're new," she said and introduced herself as Beatrice, "I'm pleased to meet you." "Hi, I'm Alex," "It's similar," she said. "Pardon?" questioned Alex. "To a university silly." "Oh yes," he said. Alex was confused.

He was being bombarded with information and some of it didn't make any sense at all. Her voice interrupted his flow: "Are you paying attention to me Alex?...Alex?" "Yes, yes of course, I'm sorry it's just." "Just," Beatrice said, "I see, it's all right, you are new aren't you?" she exclaimed.

Alex was puzzled by the fact that Beatrice looked eighteen or nineteen but FELT as though she was more than sixty! "Don't worry about it," she exclaimed, matter of factly, "I'm an old spirit, this is the last body I had. I thought you would understand, being the same, I mean?" This remark passed him by. Alex thought to himself "I don't think I'm ready for this." Beatrice interrupted: "Maybe, not yet," she said.

He tried to collect his thoughts. "How could you appear younger than you are?" he said, "It just doesn't make any sense, not that sort of age gap." "Well, to simplify greatly, you must understand that we have many lives...or in fact one." "I thought this was simple?" questioned Alex.

41

His mind could not take it all in. "Look, it's all very easy, living many lives gains us many experiences, this gives us what can be explained as a type of maturity and whereas some are only beginning a road of experience, others have travelled further," she said.

"I see, but what about one life?" (He was determined to catch her out.) "Oh that!" She laughed and tossed her head back; her hair shone in the sunlight. "We have this existence which incorporates all the other lives of experiences, like a diamond with all of its facets being polished one by one."

To be quite frank this stunned him to a high degree; it was not the earth-shattering answer he was expecting. In fact, its arrangement was so beautifully simple that, after expecting an answer to mystify Einstein, he actually felt quite stupid.

If he could blush, he was sure he was doing so now and that everybody could see! He realised that being so simple and an example of God's work seemed to fit so well together. He was amazed it was not obvious before, he turned away. "You can't hide your feelings like that you know." He knew that too, but having forgotten, embarrassed him even more.

"I'm sorry, being an older spirit, I thought you would have known?" *That* remark again. He was embarrassed again: "Really made to look stupid now," he thought, "not knowing things I should." He whirled round.

"You," he said looking straight at her, "Miss high and mighty have embarrassed me three times in as many minutes. I'm sorry we are not all as clever as you, but some of us have regard for others' feelings and the fact that someone may be new and not sure, but at least we have patience."

"Well sir," she said, raising her voice to match his. "I just have to inform you we don't have TIME here and you're a fine one to talk about patience and one more thing... I'm sorry," she whispered and smiled, "I really am, it was awful of me, I don't know why I did it, guess I'm only human after all!" She smiled sweetly at him.

His anger went, it was unusual for him to be quick tempered and he regretted it. "Friends?" she said "Friends," he replied. "Have you been here many times?" he asked. "To the library?" she said with a smile, "Of course!" he said, becoming frustrated again.

"Yes," she said, "a few times, I think books are great, you can learn so much about anything and everything. What are you interested in?" He wasn't sure, well he was, but it wouldn't come to mind.

He had the feeling the relevant material would be pointed out. "Oh lots of things, anything really, whatever takes my fancy, is it big inside?" he nodded toward the door. "Big isn't exactly the word, but it's bigger than it looks," she replied.

The twenty or thirty steps to the front doors gave a feeling of reducing the building, of making it a personal place, one where you felt at home.

"I suppose it must be?" he remarked. "What?" she said. He looked at her. "Bigger than it looks." "Touché," she said. They both laughed and made their way up.

Through the entrance Alex found more doors and on turning the corridor, a desk. "Good morning," said a young man. "Morning?" questioned Alex.

"I'm sorry," said the man, "I thought you were new, it's just that I forgot myself and supposed it would be nice to welcome you that way."

"Oh that's all right, I just didn't expect it, but it does seem natural somehow. I suppose I am new, er... in a way," said Alex. They all laughed.

"Now which section do you require?" he asked. "That," said Alex, pausing for impact and resting his finger upon his lips, "is a very good question."

"Well, what interests do you have?" the man asked. Alex thought and thought, he knew his mind was working, it just seemed to be in neutral, the thought and speech part seemed OK, his memory appeared to be completely blank.

He smiled in a very embarrassed way. "I think I'll, er... look around, get the feeling of the place and er... see what takes my fancy." "What a good idea," said the others. "The books are through there," the librarian said, pointing to a pair of large doors.

Alex felt very strange. "It's not like me to go blank," he thought, "I just feel so stupid." "I wouldn't worry about it Alex," said Beatrice gently, "I suppose there's a good reason for it".

She had a knowing look in her eye and Alex felt she was self-assured and confident. "Yes," he said thoughtfully, "I suppose there is" and he relaxed completely.

As he relaxed, thoughts began to reach him. At first he wasn't sure if it were other people's, giving him directions, but then he decided that it was his own mind sensing the sections of books before him and also particular books in those sections and even to his astonishment, words and paragraphs from those books.

As the endless stream of information came, he found himself dismissing them all one at a time, even though his interest in a particular passage here or there remained long enough for him to sense the content of the page.

His own thoughts interrupted him: "Beatrice, do we need to actually read these books?" "Well," she said, "we do, those more advanced in the higher spheres would not, the knowledge is assimilated in a similar way with that you have just experienced, but in far more detail. They would also feel the subtle changes and directions that the writer felt at the time of writing, together with a fine tone of intent behind all the words written. "It would be," she said "like reading a rainbow with all the finer colours and subtleties clearly visible. Sounds and expressions so far above Earthly feelings and so easily missed by all, even those on this Plane."

Alex recognised a hint of sadness in those words. There was a longing to progress, to experience those feelings but something was holding her back, not just her temper but also something else.

He concluded he was not to know at this time, but realised his own temper had let him down, although he noted that it had happened because he sensed her temper and feelings; at least he had learned something.

Although she was far more developed than him Beatrice had a long way to go. This made him feel sad. How much further had he to go? And yet, this reinforced his longing to progress.

"I fear things are not always what they seem or appear to be and that there are many lessons to learn even in little things. I can see there are and will be many difficulties to overcome." He mused his thoughts over.

"Alex," a voice interrupted, "you have learned an important lesson." The voice slowly brought him round.

Beatrice's voice had gently come into focus; it was the only way he could describe it and he had been somewhere else in his thoughts while walking and talking with her.

Nothing of importance had been missed and everything had been gained from this contact. He was to experience this contact more; this he knew and he took comfort from it.

Beatrice was pointing out various sections and subjects, Alex noted everything was symmetrical, lots of neat rows of bookcases. Here and there, chairs and tables for comfort and ease of reading. "Old habits die hard," he said to himself.

As he looked into the distance the bookcases seemed to get infinitely smaller. He turned and looked to each side and also behind. It was the same view in each direction. Rows and rows and rows of books. This made him feel giddy, not only the sheer size but also that it appeared like a maze!

"How could anyone possibly find a book that they wanted?" he gasped. His exasperation tickled Beatrice and the others around him. Alex shushed them. "This is a library," he said, wide-eyed, "shush!"

It only increased the mirth. "Oh Alex, you're not on Earth now! This is a happy place!"

This sentence's dual meaning hit Alex quite hard. Earth in comparison was an unhappy place. Forgetting this he found himself laughing with all the rest. "But how do you find a book? It must take a lifetime to walk the corridors alone!" he said.

This only increased the laughter until some were crying tears of joy. "Oh Alex," she said, "you are *so funny*." It took a while for all concerned to resume some air of dignity. Alex was still good-humouredly puzzled.

"Well," Beatrice began, "you can either ask the librarian at the desk, or find it under the index like a normal library, or you can notice your own thoughts just like when you came in. When you know what you want your mind will lead you to it."

Alex remembered that you only had to think of a place to go there instantaneously. "Well," he said, "brilliant! I've been here ten minutes already, learnt quite a lot and not even opened a book yet."

This started more fits of laughter. "Ten minutes *already,*" mimicked Beatrice, "oh Alex, I never knew you were Jewish!" They both fell about at this remark.

"Oh God," he said, "I haven't had this much fun for ages." They both managed to calm down eventually, even with a giggle here and there. He looked through a few books, flicked over pages, his mind searching. He realised this, as though it was trying to form a word on its own to convey to him. The word 'Jewish' appeared followed very quickly by the word 'Religion.'

"Religion" he muttered to himself "Religion."

He found himself at the librarian's desk where he was aware of being given directions and instructions. He then found himself looking at a large bookcase much taller than himself. "This one section is four blocks square," he was mumbling, not sure how large a 'block' was.

His hand immediately reached up and took a book from above his head. He found a table and began to read. This procedure repeated itself until he had completed five or six books. He was concerned that although religions in the main had the same characteristics, they seemed to be unaware of the real state of things.

He pondered for a while. Words began to form again in his mind: "Flowers, scents, sense, colour, meaning, views, light, music, healing, Mediums."

The words floated by, one by one. An idea was forming. "Joan of Arc, voices, Mediums, light, colour, healing, music, senses." In a flash he was off to another section, again he knew which books to read. This process repeated itself through various sections until he thought he had "enough to think of for the moment."

In his mind he searched for Beatrice, found her and joined her. She was reading a comedy, tears rolling down her face. His thoughtful frame of mind interrupted her flow.

"Alex, you should not be so serious, laughter is good medicine!" she said. "I know," he said, "but wouldn't it be nice if we could all laugh together?"

His eyes expressed that faraway look. "There is so much to be done, so much important work." "Yes," she agreed following his line of thought, "perhaps we should go now?" He nodded: "I think it's time."

46

They parted on the steps of the library promising to meet again when the circumstances were right. He went to the ward, spoke to Maria and went for a rest. "To soak it all up."

His fitful sleep seemed so long. There were discussions, arguments for and against, reasoning's, plans being made, but most of all was a path of light in the darkness.

Promises made earlier were recalled. He knew his work had begun. His task was most important and his knowledge, old and new, must be forged into a useful tool. Strong yet razor edged, a staff for the needy and a weapon of kindness for the aggressive.

He woke slowly, bringing all these thoughts with him. Maria was attending to the woman. For a moment he caught sight of a beautiful light between them. It was so bright he had to blink, then it was gone.

"Hello there," she said without turning. "Maria, I have had the most wonderful experience, my work has been outlined, I have remembered things I do not recall knowing and also read the most wonderful books. These have given me an insight into how things are here, in the real world and how they should be on Earth.

"I am aware of knowledge old and new to be used as a shield of protection for the young, the good, the innocent and also a weapon to cut down the hypocrisy and bad thoughts, to counteract wrong doings. Maria, I want to help all God's children, young and old."

A silence fell, its presence strong, they both turned to a point of light coming slowly toward them, its colours so beautiful and yet it was white. "It's like a prism," he whispered, "showing that many parts make up the whole, a perfect blend."

The light began to form into a human shape and although intensely bright, Alex knew it had 'dimmed' itself considerably by lowering its vibrations. A woman's voice spoke and he could see a beautiful face, serene. This vision of beauty and wisdom spoke with God's love.

"Alex, your prayer has been answered. Your love and compassion will head a new era. These thoughts have reached high; it pleases all God's workers that you are willing now to undertake His work. God is with you Alex and through the many difficulties that arise, you must only ask for his help.

"Alex, you have come of age and you will shortly see yourself in your true state and the knowledge you seek will be made known."

The light of love this spirit brought was so pure and strong that when she had gone the usual glow of the Summerland seemed to have dulled. "It seems gloomy here now," he said to Maria, "even in this wonderful place." "Ah yes, but greater wonders further on," she said, smiling her precious smile, "something to work for, by helping others."

This last remark seemed to wake Alex, for he realised he was quite stunned by the experience, that this being should acknowledge him was one thing, but to greet him in this way was overwhelming.

"Maria, I must begin God's work." He realised the full importance of this statement, for it was GOD'S WORK he, as lowly as he was, had dedicated his existence to Him. He knew that, should he never be rewarded, he would still pursue this work for GOD'S greater glory.

"I now know how people feel when they have had a vision or an inspiration of God, nothing else matters. Many have pledged their word to the end of Earthly life on but a glimpse, so much good work.

"I am reminded of Joan of Arc and her voices. When Moses had these experiences he was hailed as a prophet, but poor Joan, she was burnt as a witch, when in fact all the great people have had divine inspiration and given various religions their creed." His words rang clear and true.

Chapter 4

Gypsy Boy and Other Things

Alex sat quietly for a while until at last he spoke: "Maria, I have read wonderful books, if only people knew, if only they took notice of what is obvious, we all would be so much happier."

"Well, most know, lots of people have psychic experiences and a feeling there must be something more; evidence is all around them. To an enlightened percentage it is clear however; to another the truth is suppressed.

"A few, in total ignorance or most likely a fear that they may be ridiculed or that their own beliefs, such as they are, are turned upside down and dashed; hide the truth.

"Cases of near death experiences, Mediumship, healing and other psychic and spiritual happenings are all well documented. For so long it has been assumed that spiritual experience is the sole domain of religions, whilst all other 'Psychic' happenings are implausible, yet the world (Earth) is changing.

"Scientists have discovered that far beyond the atom, the smallest part is made of light, something that Mediums have been announcing for years, Alternative medicines are beginning to work alongside 'established' medicines, when in fact the majority of drugs were used initially directly from plants.

Throughout the history of man even sickening animals (cats etc.) eat plants when they are unwell, yet it has been assumed thousands of years of 'hocus pocus' can be swept aside by a couple of hundred years of so-called 'modern' medicines, many of which, through being distilled, cause more harm than good, side effects can sometimes be horrendous. Natural medicines have little or no side effects.

"In all fields of development, God's truth surges forward, even through music yes; even music is a powerful force on its own. Much debt is owed to musicians, most recently Jimi Hendrix.

"Jimi Hendrix," gasped Alex. "Ah yes," she remarked, "an extraordinary man, not least for his qualities of Mediumship." Maria's look gained his admiration in an instant.

"You're a fan?" asked Alex. "Yes, very much so, his inspirational guitar playing was second to none and as you will find, his words gave a special message too. Mostly though," she said sadly, "these were overlooked.

"I remember a one song concert after Martin Luther King passed, it was at the Newark Auditorium and thinly disguised as a 'song for a friend.' It left the stadium in tears."

Alex could hear the music playing in her head. "You may think his playing was at times ferocious, very unspiritual, songs like 'Machine Gun' or 'Star Spangled Banner,' with all the bombs and rockets going off and the guitar screaming, sid Maria.

"However, Jimi was portraying in his 'sound pictures' the very real agony of war, the whistling of shells, the dying agonised screams of men before the final stages of passing. Although not all of his songs told of the harsh realities of war, as you have found."

"Tell me about the Star Spangled Banner. It was an instrumental wasn't it?" said Alex. "Yes, well that's very interesting, you see it's the pride of America, the National Anthem but, as was common in those days, Jimi cleverly and subtly turned it into a protest song," Maria replied.

Alex interrupted: "A protest song, how?" "It cleverly conjures up the pictures of America the beautiful, America the great, all peaceful...happy...then you see the other side of the nation; it could be any nation, again portraying the dying, those wounded in battle, the inglorious side of war. The sheer volume of power, destruction and hate." Maria's eyes filled with tears and the first tear ran slowly down her cheek. It sparkled as though instead of reflecting light it was light; it fell to the ground, bursting into a million shards of light. From where it had impacted, a beautiful flower grew.

They both turned away and walked back slowly toward the ward. A new patient was due soon, "You must read more Alex, there is so much for you to learn...did you know that colour heals?" she asked. "Yes," he said, quietly wondering why she asked such a simple question.

"Did you also know that music heals? Because each note has its own vibration and colour?" The meaning hit him directly, relaxation tapes, blues, stirring marching music, lively disco. Each with their own benefits, healing, revitalising.

His own mind ran an endless stream of possibilities and consequences. He was quiet for a time as they walked off into the distance. At last he spoke: "Maria, is there somewhere I may hear Jimi's music?" "Why of course," she said, "follow me."

She led him to a dome in a quiet endless meadow filled with flowers of all kinds of vibrant colour. "Just sit down and listen, you will hear it all." In an instant, she was gone. His mind, focusing on her disappearance, followed her to the ward.

In the background, a note stirred sweet and low. It called his mind back to his being, slowly drifting, drifting, the word 'drifting' was impressed on his mind and it introduced the song.

To Alex the words and notes were so beautiful. It played itself a few times till he 'saw' the message *Drifting, Drifting through the journey of life, lost in an endless sea of sorrow, with little chance of help, except for one saving grace (God, the lifeboat, cradling your soul). Sailing your own boat (body), making your final way home to the World of Spirit.*

Song after song played and their individual intimate meanings become clear. Here, thought Alex, was a truly great man. 'Gypsy Boy' (land of the new rising sun) was how Jimi saw himself. A messenger, spreading his story, of the new world that (Earth) could be.

'Angel' told of the passing of his own phase, of his premonition that *"Sure enough this morning came unto me."*

'Belly Button Window' gave a much more direct message, of a spirit waiting to be born to parents who do not want it. The second verse ends with the highlight that the spirit would be glad to go back to Spirit land.

'Purple Haze' and 'Third Stone from the Sun' dealt with Astral Projection and travel. 'Machine Gun' dealt with the dying moments of a young soldier.

What most impressed Alex was '1983 (A Merman I Should Turn to Be),' which told of a couple who could not face the war and gave up their bodies. All the music was a perfect blend for the words and took the listener to the point of change (passing) and beyond, the quiet meditative music building a world of serenity before the fuzz guitar slowly brought you back to your world. The songs' words held no other interpretation other than the rebirth of a soul into a new world.

Alex realised that Jimi must have known a lot about Spirit to write in this way, that was obvious...and to hold the inspirational touch long enough for recording and mixing was a touch of genius.

As these thoughts died away, Alex could hear further 'live' versions of various songs, the impact of which made him cry. "This marvellous, marvellous man, so kind and gentle, had a message to deliver and it was so largely ignored," he uttered.

Maria appeared before him. "I know, I know," she said, "it's such a shame. Did you know that Jimi was working on colour healing before he passed?" Alex shook his head. "Each note has its own colour and each colour its own healing frequency and feeling. Jimi understood this; this is why his songs have so much impact. They are timeless, as they would say on Earth," said Maria.

"He was such a good soul. That is why he was called home so young. He had learned his lessons well and coped with the experience of living the life of James Marshall Hendrix."

"My passing was so quick I did not realise, yet, so many describe pain, how can this be?" said Alex. "Well, there are many reasons for it, yet it is painless enough, the change itself," replied Maria. "I can recall many stories similar to the account I shall give you of an old lady ill asleep on her deathbed, with her relatives around her.

"Suddenly she sits upright. 'What are you doing here?' the old lady says. The relatives look around in wonder. 'There's nobody there, Gran.' 'There is, there's Jeff and Bernard, standing by the door, by that bright light,' says the old lady. As they turn to see, she falls back having passed, a beautiful moment. She goes with those who have gone before.

"Even so, there are other ways. Take, for instance, the case of a drowning person, the spirit is detached, while the body itself is thrashing about, no pain can be felt by the spirit, who is patently aware of all that is going on.

It would seem as though he/she were watching a film of himself or herself. A great relief would be felt on entrance to the World of Spirit.

"However, this is not always the case; the effects of drowning may be felt, depending on Karmic influences, which may have been imposed perhaps from a previous existence.

"These effects would be felt from outside the body. These effects may also be felt for a different reason; the person may not have finished with their Earthly existence and would have to face the condition to have existence of another world proved beyond faith.

"There are many Earthly documents to state that people have *died and returned;* their experience, therefore, is not obviously solely for the individual concerned.

"Many relate this as a religious experience, which does no harm unless their views are forced on others. *My views are right, my religion is right, it has been proved, YOU MUST follow my teaching.*

Maria went on: "Lots of people have what could be termed an unnatural fear of heights, water, dogs etc. and unless viewed from a different viewpoint some would seem to have no basis whatsoever for these conditions.

"But, they have been caused by a remembrance of a previous passing or the re-enactment of an incident from one of their past lives.

"Lots of people seriously hurt in accidents or very, very ill have the experience of being outside of their bodies watching attempts to'save' them being made. Rarely is any panic felt in that state as they are partly in the world of Spirit; usually there is a great feeling of peace, the kind they have not ever experienced in that life normally. There is an active interest in the proceedings; these people are not usually 'saved,' the usual procedure is to be met by loved ones and taken home.

"However, sudden passings and difficulties such as being materialistic or having fixed ideas of death cause problems. Also, thoughts of revenge hold people back. We shall go and see a friend of mine; he will show you something of great interest."

They came to a spot in a beautiful meadow filled with flowers of all descriptions and colours. In the centre stood a tall majestic tree, the like of which he had never seen.

"It is a species known only in the world of Spirit. Many, many things here are only of Spirit," said Maria.

Alex gazed in wonderment at the beauty of shape, not only of the tree, but each leaf was the perfect copy of the outline of the tree. Such colours shone from the tree as he never could describe. This vision touched him deeply until he realised that the tree itself was pouring forth love! Completely in harmony with its surroundings. A perfect harmony, he felt so relaxed. Perfection, just like all in the Summerland.

For a time he just listened to the birds singing and heard a butterfly's kiss as it stroked a leaf. In the distance, he could hear a babbling brook, the water's soft rhythm relaxing him more. As he listened, the splashing itself took on a musical tone, playing a lovely melodic song. "Like someone tinkling on a piano," he thought.

A lovely voice made itself known, to Alex, it's musicality strangely familiar and yet so distinct. It came from behind the tree. Maria and Alex walked around and he was surprised to see a man with, dare he think it, the face of an angel.

The love and compassion shone out in all directions from this wondrous being; somehow, he made the flowers even more beautiful with his presence. "Hello Alex, I'm Paul." Alex was too overcome to say much.

"I have come here to show you something," said Paul. The words bounced through Alex. It was the only way he could explain it - bouncing waves of love.

"An experience to contemplate upon, for the lessons are many. Will you come with me?" Alex answered in a whisper: "Yes, yes gladly." "Well then Maria, we shall see you in a space," said Paul.

His angel-like smile transfixed Alex until all he could see was Paul's head. Seconds passed and the background came again into view through a mist to a street. Once again he felt the 'streetwise' tenseness of being human, the fear of being attacked, of being alone and helpless.

His psychic senses told him he was in Glasgow, one or two smiling faces belying the underlying tension. Someone's bright aura disappeared around the corner. At first, he thought it was Paul, but no, it was incarnate.

54

His attention was drawn to a thin boy two or three streets away, walking in his direction. He mentally noted this and was then drawn to the front room of a home. The feelings within it were acidic, not so much in a spoken way, although tempers were often frayed. Violence was no stranger here, this he knew.

A young man came down the stairs and kicked open the door, singing in a thick Scottish brogue: "Tae nite's the nite, cause am feelen a-right..."

"Ye'll be feelen ma hand if ye kick the sticks (furniture) anymore." It was a women's voice. "And ye'll be getting a face full o`headies if you carry on." The man's previous smile had gone. Replaced by a snarl.

The woman knew the glint in the man's cold, cold stare. She bit her tongue. Her thoughts ran to her broken home and the feelings within it.

The vicious stare had gone, a smile returned. "Someone's going tae be lucky tae' nite," he laughed as he looked in the mirror. His mother thought: "Some girl will be unlucky to get hitched to you boy."

Alex withdrew and found himself with the thin boy; he was with a few friends in a disco pub. The atmosphere was one of what could only be described as expectancy.

Trouble was no stranger here either; Alex tried to perceive the outline of the circumstances, but it was useless. He would have to wait and see. "Leave well enough alone" became impressed on his mind and he thankfully acknowledged this.

Throughout the pub people were laughing and joking, a glass slipped to the floor. The noise level dropped. Eyes looked furtively round. With no other signal, or sound, the laughing and joking returned.

Alex was glad he passed before he experienced this type of life. "They come here for fun! A good time?" he said to himself. He felt sad that people lived like this.

In the back of his mind, he wondered why people put up with it. His thoughts ran to a phone box where a phone had been slammed down. "Whoo whoo, were gonna have some fun tae' nite." It was the other man. An arrangement had been made.

On the face of it all seemed well, but Alex felt uneasy. He was too aware of his psychic feelings to dismiss them. Alex knew something was about to happen. The man was making his way here and meeting friends.

Alex soaked up the atmosphere. It was in its own way electric. The air of expectancy drew all kinds of people - villains, or people who wanted 'in.' People who wanted others to think of them as villains or hard cases. People who wanted others to know this was their watering hole. This attracted girls who liked dangerous men. Lots of girls. This in turn brought men who wanted to meet girls. The whole thing was a sad circle.

Alex had categorised not only the place, but some of its customers. This included the skinny boy, whose name he was not to know and also the other man James, James McArdle. A nice name for someone who was distinctly the opposite. James was thirty, reddish hair with a broken nose and a strong chin. Tall and muscular as fighters normally are, he bore small scars from many battles.

Only guessing at the outcome of a meeting between these two parties, Alex began to feel sorry for the thin one. A firm thought asked him to "Bestill your troubled mind."

At last, James had come in with two friends and they met others. Eight in total. The fun in their minds was a fight, trouble, bad trouble; a group had been picked out. It included the thin one.

James could always be relied upon. A Glaswegian hard man. But tonight someone else was to start the proceedings off. Half draining their glasses, they slowly gathered round this group, one at a time. A jog here, a push there. It had begun.

The fun started and James took a dislike - and a glass - to the thin one. Somehow, his well practised aim missed. The young boy threw his left arm in the air, distracting him. What happened next began in slow motion.

A knife was pulled from the boy's back pocket and the button pressed. In one steady movement the blade slid out, locking a split second before biting.

The initial prick made James catch his breath. Quarter of an inch. Half an inch. One inch. Two and a half inches. The full four and a half inches glided between his ribs. For a split second, it felt cold, but was then replaced by a burning hot sensation.

James thought he had been punched, quite hard. The arm was withdrawn, along with the blade, which remained hidden from view in the palm of a hand.

The boy ran, James ran after him, but the boy was faster and became lost in the back streets. "I know you son," James shouted at the top of his voice. "I'll have ye."

He went back to the pub to see how the others fared. The commotion soon told him someone had been murdered. "Nay doubt that's one tae us," he smiled, "I'll have the other bastard to me sel."

In the distance, the familiar sounds of police sirens. "Think I'll have me-sel a wee dram," he said and sidled off into a bar a half mile away and found a space next to a friend. "John, I've been here all night, ye understand me?"

As no grunt of disapproval greeted him, he relaxed and looked around. Quite a crowd, no one would ever know. It was only when he couldn't get the barman's attention with and without the usual banter and threats that he realised something was amiss. No one could see or hear him. It came as a bit of a shock, even so he thought he would go home and sleep it off.

Unlocking the door, he made his way up to bed for a fitful sleep. A short time later came a hammering on the front door; he knew it well.

"Mrs McArdle, open up it's the *po'lice.*" His mother stirred from the next room and stuck her head out of the window. "What dae ye want noo?"

The answer came: "We have some business wi ye, can we no come in?" Not again, she thought. "Aye if ye must." The front door was opened.

"I'm afraid we've a bit o` bad news for ye, Mrs McArdle, ye might need a seat." James crept to the landing. His mother sat on the edge of the settee, James crept up to the living room door, expecting to be called at any moment.

"We'er afraid it's Jimmy, his been kill't, murdurd." Shocked his mother may have been, but it was an understatement to what James felt.

He burst through the door, his mind in turmoil, shouting at the top of his voice: "Ye silly bastards, what kinda joke is that?" No one heard. No one noticed.

He ran upstairs to his bedroom. His bed had not been slept in! James had begun to form a fog in his mind and this began to envelope him physically. Alex became aware that they had moved location and he had become entangled in James's thoughts.

They were walking the streets, both completely cut off in the fog. The oppressed feeling became too strong for Alex and struggle as he might, he could not free himself. All the feelings and emotions of this psychopath began to wear him down.

Panic was rising in him. Whatever he tried, nothing worked. Like James, his mind was becoming a one track thought - HATE...HATE...HATE. James looked as though he was becoming more powerful... and quite mad.

With the panic slowly rising, Alex managed to squeeze one thought out - "Maria." This led quickly to thoughts of Paul. Immediately a beacon shone in the swirling grey mass, this point of light slowly coming nearer until Paul appeared.

Alex's fearful look left him as Paul smiled and together they went upward. "Do you remember all the details Alex?" he quietly asked. Alex nodded. "The oppression was fearful," he said, deep in thought, "but the feeling of helplessness was the worst."

Paul turned around in front of him. "But those were your own feelings Alex, because you know the light and have perceived a fraction of the truth. The other feelings were your companions. But he is for the time being happy in his environment.

"This place he has made for himself, did you notice how easily you were drawn into his world? This is partly due to your compassion for him. For what he is about to go through, but also because you, resembling the murderer in build, were reaching out to each other in an incorrect way.

"You will be taught to help these people and it requires patience and love... Alex interrupted: "Love? ...but how can you love someone like that?" Paul smiled his beautiful smile. "Who are we to judge, Alex?"

"This poor creature will learn to come up from the depths he has dug himself into, to forgive and love the murderer." Alex could see his own task was much simpler than James's.

He also knew he had so very much to learn. He looked at Paul. "I'm so very sorry for what I said; I have witnessed the feelings of God's love for all. He denies us nothing yet I would deny this pitiful being, this spirit called James McArdle, I would condemn him with my own thoughts."

Alex's emotions swelled and tears formed: "GREAT FATHER, DIVINE SPIRIT, forgive me for my sin. Teach me to truly love my neighbour."

His shining silver tears fell onto his feet where they formed a puddle of light, which somehow drew itself up inside him, purifying him.

What he did not know was that a few beads of light made their way down toward James's abode, illuminating, ever so slightly, the darkness. Paul left him at the tree and Maria greeted him: "Come Alex, we have a new arrival."

The woman Maria had previously attended had gone. In her place was a young man, a victim of a motorbike accident. He slept peacefully enough. Alex gazed at him for ages, aware that another part of this young man's conscience 'drifted off' every now and then.

Alex's s quiet mood stirred with Maria's voice. "He has been to see his parents. He is not happy about the autopsy." She paused and added by way of explanation: "The authorities thought it might be drink or drugs as no one else was involved and no reason seemed to fit for the incident."

Maria changed the subject sharply: "Did you not learn much from your visit with Paul?" Alex nodded dolefully whilst remembering his selfish thoughts on those matters.

"At least you have learned, James must help himself and look to the light before we are able to help him. We cannot, of course, interfere with his freewill, we must wait until he looks away from his surroundings and searches for something else." This had interceded Alex's question. "I would say a fair space," she continued, "would elapse. Do you remember how you were drawn into his world?"

Alex did not need reminding. Maria said: "This happens when in the body." Alex puzzled at this, wondering if he had interpreted the comment correctly "In the body?"

He mused. "Yes," replied Maria, "and sadly all too often. If you help me for a while we shall then take a trip, a bit nicer this time." She had sensed Alex's apprehension.

Chapter 5

Spooks and Vampires

The rest home and its occupants being seen to, Maria beckoned to Alex to follow. "This time we must be quiet," she said, "we must only observe. Guard your thoughts closely, many energies will be near."

Alex did not like the implications of the word *energies*. It had a distinctly non-human sound and feel. "Some are not, never have been, but do not worry, we are protected," Maria said.

Her thoughts went firmly into Alex's mind, almost as if it had been shouted. She took his hand and away they went down, down to a swirling mist, his apprehension calmed by the gentle squeeze of her hand.

Once again, he felt the difficulty of movement and knew they were close to Earth. Onward they went into the darkness. In the distance Alex could see several points of light, some brighter than others, in the rough form of a circle.

As they approached, Alex could see ten people sitting at a table. "Oh go on Jenny, it won't work unless we all do it. Go on...it's only a game, just a bit of a laff." Egged on, she finally agreed thus encouraging the last two.

"Right, before we start there is a procedure," said a boy who appeared to be in charge. "Dim the lights?" said a hopeful voice "Bloody hell no, much more important than that, who wants a refill?" This brought a roar of approval from all concerned.

As some left for drinks, Alex noticed that a board lay in the centre of the table. On this board was a word. "Ou...Oui...Ouija...Ouija board!" He looked at Maria nervously.

She was looking around, sensing in the darkness. He focused as she did. The silence in this dimension was broken by scratching and fumbling. Noises of all sorts. In the distance, he swore he could hear a cackle, a hideous laugh.

Once again, all had resumed their seats. A tumbler was placed on the board. "Right then, who's going to start?" said a voice. "Go on Ben, you've done it before," said another.

False modesty broke into a broad grin. "Yeah, what the hell." He took a swig from his glass and put it down. "Is anybody there?" he spoke in his spookiest voice, "is anybody there?...... one tap for yes..... two for no."

More laughter. "Is anybody there.....? Anybody will do....as long as it's not the bogeyman." More laughter. A hand touched a head. "Oh my God," said a girls voice, "I can feel something, shivers up my spine." The hand yanked her hair, "You bastard, you scared me!" Another voice spoke up: "And I thought it was his hand on your backside!"

More laughter. "Come on, come on, let's be a bit more serious. Now everybody place a finger on the glass." A spirit drew near. "Is there anybo...." The glass moved.

A hush fell, with whispers here and there. "Hope it's not Dracula." A giggle. The spirit introduced himself as George, someone who had 'spoken' to Ben before.

Meaningless questions were answered, the spirit drawing facts from the sitters, phrasing them in such a way as the present company expected.

Alex saw that this had the effect of *opening up* some of the sitters, brightening their auras, increasing their light. This attracted more spirits from what Alex could only guess were miles around.

By this point in time, a few of the sitters were feeling uneasy. The jokes were still being cracked, but mainly to lighten up the atmosphere. Jenny stood up: "I don't want to do this." Her light dimmed. "I want to stop." She sat on the sofa lighting a cigarette. "Scaredy cat, scaredy cat," a voice taunted.

George moved the glass a letter at the time. "S...C...A...R...E...D...Y.....C...A...T." One or two of the sitters thought this not funny at all and removed their fingers from the bottom of the glass.

George spelled some more. "S...O.....W...H...O...S...E..... S...C...A...R...E...D.....N...O...W?" All but two removed their fingers.

More spelling. "S...O....W...H...A...T...A...B...O...U...T..... Y..O...U.....T..W..O....A...R...S...E...H...O..L...E...S?" Both fingers were now removed and the light dimmer turned up.

A scream brought everybody's attention to the moving glass. Someone screamed: "Jesus H Christ." Everyone was transfixed. The glass moved some more.

"W...R...O...N...G.....G...U...E...S...S.....A...G...A...I...N."

The temperature in the room dropped; more power, more spirits came, more power.

George was having a really good time. Chuckling in a hideous fashion. "I...S.....N...O.....O...N...E.....G...O...I...N...G.... T...O.....G...U...E...S...S?....N...O...T.....O...N...E....O...F.....Y...O...U... ...A...R...S...E...H...O...L...E...S."

Someone moved toward the board to close it up but was pushed away by one of George's accomplices. The glass shattered into powder.

George and his friends had disappeared. Alex could see now that kindly spirits had intervened, frustrating George and keeping the sitters safe from permanent harm.

Maria spoke: "They have had a shock; it should keep them from taking such matters lightly, at least most." Her gaze was directed at Ben.

The party broke up and everyone left. Maria and Alex followed Ben... along with George and one or two accomplices. Ben was thinking about George. This allowed George to draw nearer.

"Arseholes," Ben muttered, "bunch of arseholes, we had something then, something powerful and *they* blew it." Alex noticed that George had been drawing facts from Ben, pieces of information that would form a puzzle of George's choosing. Pieces which looked innocent, until they were all finally together.

Pieces of this puzzle had already been fed to Ben and he was already hooked. George spoke to a part of Ben that listened.

A heady mix of ego, a small amount of mediumistic power (that would take years of training to develop properly) and a lot of the frailties of character of this poor soul.

Alex remembered a passage from a book "...we must never forget that like attracts like, more so in the World of Spirit, but also on the Earth plane, this is the law and must always be remembered when incarnate in the body and trying to contact Spirit.

"Good mediumship takes years to develop; lots of hard work carried out unselfishly and must only be attempted under the strictest conditions.

"Should there be any desire other than the love of the people of the world then your thoughts would hinder your development and endanger your physical and mental health and consequently others also..."

He realised from this that the spirit who called himself George and Ben must be quite alike and from what he saw of George, thought a dislike of Ben was justified.

Alex listened to George's words. "Bunch of arseholes, don't they know a thing? Couldn't they feel the power? Lots of it and I (Ben) was in control of it.

"I only broke the glass because they made me mad. It was only my power." These words sifted through Ben's mind as if they were his own.

So carefully phrased, with just the right amount of emotion, so readily accepted as his own. "I'll try again later, no need to rush, must conserve my power for now."

Ben felt powerful. Self assured. He whistled his way home, expectation in his heart...and mind. Alex became fretful and moved away. "Maria, this is so dangerous, can't we do something?" She sadly looked at him.

"In this case we cannot, but we must not forget the huge amount of others in the same position, it is not our task to help this way, these souls must live their existences.

"They must learn from their own mistakes. It is for their own progression. Our work lies in a different direction,"

"Maria, has this Ben agreed to this abuse in Spirit before being incarnate?" said Alex. "Well, this needs the answer yes and no," replied Maria. "You see, through the course of incarnation certain tasks will need to be faced. These are agreed beforehand for your own good. NO challenge is ever given that you cannot master. Once these tasks are accomplished successfully they never need be faced again ever. If, however, you cannot overcome the obstacle it will be faced again; perhaps in a future incarnation, if not this one, usually the task will be harder.

"The tasks vary in number and difficulty; however, a large portion of freewill is given. Why are we given tasks when incarnate? The answer is simple. As you know, a more accurate observation of events is possible from here and the necessity of the tasks and benefits of progression are seen much clearer, which is why they are agreed to. Of course, the circumstances on Earth may seem insurmountable but, as we have said, all tasks are capable of being accomplished if one takes a detached view of the details, but do not worry Alex, more and more people are becoming aware of spirit.

"The churches are filling, not only with older Spiritualists but also a younger generation, who have a healthy outlook on life and a fine discerning mind. One needs an open mind, one which questions everything before it is finally realised that other worlds exist.

"Once people realise that a person will be held responsible for their actions, ultimately, regardless of whether Earth justice has been evaded or not, is the time that conditions on Earth will improve in leaps and bounds.

"It is not to say that all religions will cease, as most advocate a 'reward' system for good living, but that they will live alongside all men in unity.

"The world as a whole has come to the realisation through countless facts submitted by learned minds incarnate and discarnate through mediums that there is, to paraphrase, *'MORE BETWEEN HEAVEN AND EARTH THAN MAN CAN SURELY KNOW.'* That, this is now known by more people is indisputable.

"Since Mankind began, he has had a sense of a *greater power* instilled within him, whichever name we have chosen to call it. The world is improving, Alex, in a way that all will see."

Alex pondered the many questions and answers that came to him. It seemed after all that justice did prevail, its law perfect, so that a criminal who smiles as he has 'plea bargained' or somehow evaded what he called justice had not in fact 'cheated in the game.'

Alex took great comfort from this, not from the point of view that justice would finally be done, but rather that all people's small kindnesses throughout life would also receive justice. It was a wondrous sight to behold and fearful in its purpose.

Alex finally realised that all was *taken into account*. As they made their way back to the ward, he questioned his own life and thoughts, remembering that *the mind is God's camera,* capturing all and he was daunted by his own shortcomings.

The prospect of entering the temple of truth gave full meaning to *like attracts like* and *rewards and punishment for deeds done* and *most profoundly, your sins shall find you out.*

A thought drifted down to him, that reparation be made through working for the good of others. He knew it would be harder for others than for him through his short life.

Alex took a long walk through meadows and forests. Quietening his mind and assimilating the recent events, he looked forward to his next lesson.

Chapter 6

The Meeting

Of late, Alex had been busying himself in the ward. Lots of people had come and gone. He had visited the library on a couple of occasions and also the theatre. He was astounded by the real truth of matters once the lies, deceit and propaganda had been stripped away.

He had been talking to his mother whilst she had been sleeping and although everything was understood, it was *erased* when she woke.

Maria had explained that this was a normal process with many good reasons behind it and once explained, Alex agreed it made good sense. Still, it left him a little unhappy that his mother could not be afforded a direct contact.

Maria had made enquires and told him that a meeting would be arranged and he would be informed in due course of the occasion; sure enough it arrived.

Alex was more than curious as to what form it would take and his patience was well tested as Maria had kept the details from him for a special reason.

It was, he later found out, that for him to experience the occasion 'first hand' was necessary and prior knowledge would lessen the effect of the experience. Only the time was given to him - 8.14.

To Alex it seemed an eternity. As time was not important in the Summerland, he had no way of judging how long to go.

Maria finished her work and went to meet him. He had been reading a book of poems, one of which was entitled 'Summerland.' He had just finished it as Maria appeared. "It is time Alex," she said. He did not need asking twice.

They made their way close to Earth and Alex found himself at the back of a hall. Maria stood quietly by. It seemed as though a speaker were addressing an audience, but Alex could not make out what was happening.

He saw lots of spirit people drawing close to their loved ones. Some had one or two friends or relatives, others appeared to have whole families going back generations, including cats and dogs, a sheep and a parrot!

Some spirit people were forming queues while others who appeared to be talking through intermediaries, were in a fairly large group. Alex turned his attention to the speaker, who stood near the front of a small stage.

To his right and behind sat a small squat woman who almost appeared to be asleep. Just behind the speaker stood a tall well-built yet elegant figure of an Egyptian, who seemed to be in charge.

Behind him and to his left were three or four figures, who were mixing some kind of chemicals. Alex could see that a lot of power was built up around the speaker, who was nevertheless having trouble.

As Alex drew nearer, he could see a *veil of consciousness* between the spirit people and the speaker and his assistants. There was a young girl and a helper, who was trying to get their thoughts across to the speaker, who was talking to a middle-aged woman with ginger hair.

"I have a young girl here, aged around eight, who is wearing a red dress," said the speaker. This puzzled Alex, as her clothes were not red! The thought went out again. "I'm sorry madam, she is holding a huge red beach ball." Now the speaker filled in with his own interpretation: "She is taking me back to a holiday, some time ago."

The recipient was thinking hard, she understood the little girl but not the ball. "I'm sorry," said the woman, "could you clarify for me?" The little girl sent the thought again.

This time the speaker thought hard; the symbol of a beach ball always meant holidays to him. "Yes, I'm sure it's a holiday." The woman thought hard, her little girl never had a beach ball. "No, I'm sorry," she said, "I can take the little girl, but not the beach ball."

To Alex it seemed a protracted conversation. The helper spoke to the girl and then to the Egyptian who, using mind pictures, asked the speaker to relax and concentrate. The thought went out again with the emotion of *missing*.

The speaker spoke again: "I'm sorry my love, we do not appear to be communicating very well tonight. This is a young girl aged about eight, she is showing herself to me wearing a swimming costume and holding a large red ball, but she appears to be sad."

The woman thought again and after a 'nudge' by the girl, her memories came back. "Yes, of course, I see it now." Her face lit up. "I lost my little girl about twelve years ago. At that time we had little money and promised our Sylvia a holiday and a big red beach ball, which sadly she never got. Thank you, thank you, God bless you Sylvia." The woman was now smiling contentedly; however, she had now preempted more information being given by Sylvia, so the speaker had no choice but to go to someone else.

Alex was beckoned forward by the Egyptian, as the speaker drank a glass of water, refilled and drank again. As Alex stepped past the veil, the speaker spoke: "I would like to come to you madam, fourth row back, white jumper, that's it, you madam," he said as she pointed to herself.

"I have a young boy here, aged about fifteen, he has shortish brown hair and is wearing a school uniform." Alex was stunned! The man could see him! Somehow, he had brought his school uniform with him.

"Unfortunately, he isn't saying a lot, but his uniform is torn in various places and his cap is missing, can you place him?"

Alex recognised the choked answer. He whirled round to see his mum. He spoke to her: "Mum, Mum, it's me, Alex." A voice interrupted his: "I'm sorry madam, he's fading a little because he's moving around a lot." This brought him smartly to attention; he wasn't going to waste his chance. He stood before the speaker. "Hello, I'm Alex," he announced. This was ignored.

"Madam does the appearance of the uniform have a meaning for you?" the speaker said.

Alex turned to face his mother. "Yes, it was an accident about five years ago." "And the cap?" asked the speaker. "Yes, that's right, he never liked wearing the cap," said his mother.

Alex faced the speaker again. "My name is Alex; I lived about eight miles from here." "He tells me his name is Alex, or Alexander."

Alex looked skyward in disgust.

"I think he preferred Alex though," said the speaker. Alex poked his tongue out at him and the man smiled. His mother answered: "Alex is correct, he hates Alexander." "Yes, I thought so, he just poked his tongue out at me." His Mother laughed: "Yes, he was always doing that."

Alex told him lots of things and also that he was glad she and Dad were together again; all was faithfully reproduced except the last part, which the speaker altered to: "He's glad everything's okay again," which his mother understood.

Alex wished her well for the coming birthday and anniversary and asked the speaker to explain he 'gave' her a big bunch of her favourite red roses, then it was time to go.

He stepped behind the veil and went to Maria. "Aren't mediums wonderful? he said. "Oh yes," she sighed wearily, "wonderful." Alex noted the veil had a very important purpose. It formed a barrier, which kept order so the medium did not get a barrage of unconnected faces and thoughts; queuing also enforced this. It was quite an orderly occasion although very busy.

He realised that giving and receiving messages was not by any means straightforward but the experience was both enjoyable and informative. He noted too that spirits tended to present themselves as they were agewise before the change, or at a particular stage in their existences.

This is why the young girl (who was in Spirit for twelve years) had projected the thought of being eight and obscured by a red beach ball, which the medium had mistaken for a red dress.

The presentation of age was quite important because the uninitiated needed a description they could remember or relate to and did not realise that, all being perfect in this sphere, people slowly came to a period when age, appearance and ability is at an optimum.

This means that spirit children grow older and older persons normally get younger. Therefore, to describe an eight-year-old child as a young woman would be most confusing.

Descriptions are all right for focusing the mind; however, the message itself is the important thing as it gives proof in a special way.

Alex stayed to the end of the meeting, which had not gone as well as the speaker had hoped; still Alex's message was perfect. The Egyptian spoke to Alex for a short time, explaining some of the difficulties of communication to him.

It was so surprising that all the many variations or variables had to coincide to make communications strong and understood.

"We all know of the feeling of talking to someone not on our wavelength, but to explain to that person your idea through a third person gives you a comparison of what can occur, even with conditions themselves being perfect," the Egyptian explained.

Alex thought about the confusion the beach ball had caused, with each of the three parties having their own idea of the meaning. Alex thanked him for his helpful explanation and bid him God's peace wherever he would go.

Turning to Maria, they made their way back.

Alex discovered on the way that a short string of *COINCIDENCES* had led his mother to the meeting that night, these all being Spirit influenced, the details of which had all been known far in advance.

Alex worked for ages in the happy knowledge that his thoughts had been expressed in a tangible and provocative way, inspiring his mother's mind. Helping to produce an effect of confidence in a God or super being adorning a place in heaven that HE was looking after her son, that death was not the end.

With Earth time passing quickly, he decided to visit his mother more although his thoughts were always with her and hers with him. He found the knack of always being aware of times of pressure and happiness. It was always comforting.

Although it was no special gift for him alone, it did seem personal. Its purpose (wonderfully constructed) was twofold, it also enabled loved ones to inspire and guide their nearest and dearest on Earth to help positively through pain or painful decisions.

This mechanism in turn caused pain to ones in Spirit for, freewill operating as ever, close ones had to watch as mistakes were made that could be avoided.

Mistakes, which affected a few, were bad enough but to watch a relative or friend deliberately turn to crime or a violent act was heartbreaking. Alex pondered the influence of guides, or as they were fancifully called, *Guardian Angels,* their roles to guide or influence their charges when they could.

Although interference in freewill was not possible, it was more a method of adding an option or view from another angle to the problem. This being presented in sleep state, or more dramatically, people would hear distinctly and loudly their name called just in time to save them from some catastrophe, the reason being that their work or learning process had not been completed up to that point. Others may have a strong sense of mistrust or foreboding about a person or adventure.

It was extremely interesting to Alex to find out that the guides who are appointed to us are surprisingly like ourselves. Having had to cope at some time or other with the same shortfalls, inclinations and weakness as ourselves, they know from personal experience the problems we face and how easy it is to fall prey to those feelings. These guides are, of course, far different to the ones with the roles of guides to a medium.

Alex was surprised to learn that different guides are with us through different stages of the incarnation, so that many may be present through that period, often *overlapping* each other.

He had not met his guide and did not know whether they were male or female. It was by no means certain they would ever meet. This spirit, in any case, was once again incarnate in the body.

It was a process which fascinated Alex and one he wished to view from afar as he never wished to leave the Spirit World again. Try as he might, he could not find a book in the library on this subject.

This he learned was by another wonderful and natural law, which states: "That knowledge will be assimilated only when the moment and person is ready."

He thought about this readily and often until the answer came by intervention. "If you knew all that the spirits in the higher planes knew, but did not progress enough to use fully or properly, it would not benefit you one iota.

"If you were to understand or have a fuller knowledge of the divine spirit before you were prepared for it, it would be like knowing all that God knew, your being could never withstand it and you would be destroyed forever through the massive expansion of the mind. Each must learn at his own pace!" the voice added, "remember, it took our Lord three days to ascend to the right hand of our Father."

This now took on a completely new meaning for Alex and reminded him of the amount of knowledge in this sphere alone. He laughed to himself at the trouble he had had with the eleven plus "I could just about cope with that," he remarked to himself.

He also remembered the experiences he'd had not long after entering Spirit, where he had been shown processes and made promises, few of which were yet emerging.

Thinking out loud once again, he said: "I suppose even a quarter of the knowledge here would be the equivalent of a four-year-old taking a dozen *S* level subjects - quite easily out of range and comprehension." "Just so," replied a familiar voice.

It was Maria. "To understand things to that degree is beyond our comprehension, for now." Maria asked Alex what he had learned from recent events. He paused thoughtfully for a while before he spoke:

"I have learned like attracts like. This being so draws individuals and groups together like magnets. Like magnets, we are able to repel or attract spirits whether incarnate or not. These spirits discarnate can and will use their influence on us when welcomed, whether it is done so knowingly or not.

"I have noticed that spirits of bad intent feed their victims with the *food* of their particular desire. They also create desire, which the individual is not averse too. This gives them greater power and therefore control over the victim, who is led on a constantly downward path, but who still has knowledge of right and wrong.

"Eventually, in severe cases, the victim may be suppressed in its body (possession) or may be forced to share, resulting in schizophrenia or madness of varying degrees (though not all madness is as a result of intervention). *Please see the work of Dr Emma Bragdon, PhD.*

"Not every case is bad. Mediums are persons specially adapted to *tune* into Spirit with the giving and receiving of information of varying levels or degrees. Physical mediums (trance) consent to being replaced in their bodies by a tried and trusted guide for the benefit of 'direct' information to individuals. Others who enable direct voice or instruments to be played, or objects moved, or for Spirit to become visible to those who are not mediums, this means that 'normal' people, those without these gifts, can experience the wonder of this form of contact.

"Very gifted mediums are rare but becoming more and more less so. Much more common is the ability to have inspiration, sometimes to the level of genius."

Alex stopped as the faraway look in his eyes drifted slowly away. He had been receiving information from another source whilst speaking. Some of it worried him, the rest exited him. His work was soon to begin in earnest. This was good; however, he now knew it would involve contact with the lower spirits, some much lower.

His work would involve rescue of Earth-bound spirits - some of those dazed and confused and those who in the lower regions who had finally looked to the light. These souls would be guarded by those more bestial than themselves, those who would feed on the torturous emotions of those that saw the spark of love but were dragged away from it.

This work was for those who unswervingly followed the light, whose every action, word and thought was influenced solely by LOVE. This is what worried Alex; he thought he was not up to it. "Why now?" he thought, why now? I have so much to learn. I am as unsteady as a child taking its first steps." He sent out a thought: "Great Father, Divine Spirit, I am willing yet find myself unable to take on this work. I feel too weak to help others stronger than myself I..."

His thoughts were interrupted by a blinding light that appeared behind a tree. This light was so bright that the tree was immersed in light, almost disappearing. It subdued itself until it was bearable and a man walked from behind the tree. He brought with him a gentleness that could be felt, this was the only way Alex could describe it. The sense of quiet authority and love literally shone from him.

Alex noticed his long elegant limbs, his bright shining eyes... and his beard. Alex was transfixed; his mind could only receive love as this figure walked toward him.

"Holy Father...," began Alex. "Now now Alex, calm down." The voice soothed Alex as nothing ever did before. "I have come to see you directly to calm your worried mind. We have His work before us. I have come to let you know that you are part of a group that has great work ahead of it.

This will be your training. We are all looking after you, no harm can befall you, your place eventually will be with us Alex, on the higher levels. You will meet colleagues to work with here but you are destined for great, great work. Soon you will recognise yourself for what you are.

I am not who you think I am, for I am far too lowly. Names are not important; I am one of your guides. You may call me Brother William. Should you ever require our help just call me and we will help directly."

He walked forward and placed his hand upon Alex's head. Such love, such healing, a surging of power raced through Alex that he could only compare it with being on your deathbed one minute and bounding with energy the next. This being had revitalised all of his body. "We shall see each other soon Alex, be of good heart, God is with you." In an instant he was gone.

Alex was so overcome that tears of joy ran down his face. He felt compelled to walk and as he did so, beautiful flowers sprang up from where his tears fell, leaving a narrow bed of flowers behind him. His feeling of love and comfort so powerful in him that it was a short space before Alex realised that his ordinary clothes had gone to be replaced by something resembling a toga. It was red and blue, the hues of which were so bright and lively they seemed almost to have a life of their own. The material was so fine it actually felt pleasant to the touch.

It had its own vibration that was perfectly compatible with Alex's and actually held the love with which it was given. A thought reached him: "A present from us to you."

Alex met Maria, her slight smile told him she'd known all along. "God bless you Alex, your work is to begin in earnest." He smiled and looked at her. Somehow she was different.

Alex knew then that Maria had been guiding him since he came over. Her teachings and knowledge had been passed to him in such a gentle and unassuming way, so subtly that at times he was almost unaware.

Maria's job was now done. Her work culminating in preparing and helping him. The change Alex could see was the emergence of a finer body so she could rise to the next plane.

He spoke to her gently, with love flowing out to her in an undying bond: "God bless you Maria, for all your work. You have helped many like myself and our gratitude is eternal."

"It's for me to thank you Alex, for providing the path of progression for me to tread. For allowing me to help and learn myself," said Maria, however, this is not goodbye, we shall find each other whenever possible. You will follow me Alex and soon I shall take you to the next plane to show you where your progression leads."

A beautiful sister of mercy appeared, who introduced herself as Clara. She and Maria talked for a while before they gently faded away.

Alex was pleased with his new clothes. It was a sign of his spiritual progression. As he now took more trips to the library and theatre, he slowly realised that lots of other people chose to wear their spiritual clothes.

One lecture in particular drew Alex's attention. It was on the attainment of a higher life and life in the next sphere. He sat in a large auditorium amongst quite a large crowd. The speaker introduced herself and began. The words she spoke, Alex had heard before, this time however, the words had a *fuller meaning*. They spurred him on and set fire to his imagination.

It seemed they were spoken to him, for him. Of course, it wasn't so, it *just felt that way*. Alex left the building with plenty to think about. Here, at last, it seemed within reach. It was attainable.

He had noticed a change within himself. It had started almost imperceptibly but now he knew it. There was restlessness, a wanting to progress, onward, upward. His work was not enough, although of late he had pursued it with more vigour, it was still not enough. He knew he could be happier in the sphere above, not that he was unhappy, no one ever really could be here, it's just that there was more.

"Just so," said a familiar voice. Alex turned to welcome Maria. "I have been with you and your thoughts of late Alex. Your work will truly begin now. Remember to serve others as you would yourself; it is the only way to progress, through service Alex, through service." They chatted for a while before Maria announced: "I am to take you to my home, to show you what you are working for."

She took his hand and they appeared in a beautiful cottage like the ones on his plane but much better. It took a while to get used to the finer vibrations and even so the experience was very tiring.

She showed him the places she loved. To Alex it seemed as though he had just stepped into Heaven. Its beauty stunned him, words failed. Having tired quickly, Maria said to Alex that they would go back.

They arrived at Alex's favourite spot, its beauty now somewhat tainted. "Oh Maria, I thought this place ever so wonderful, so beautiful and bright but now in comparison it seems so drab."

"Yes, it would seem so, but this world still has great beauty. The difference is for a reason Alex. It gives you and all those here a longing to progress, to draw nearer to God. The greater beauty there is because of the expression of His will. A greater expression being nearer to Him.

"Your reward will be progression of your soul, onward, upward, through this sphere and to others far higher. Those of which I have barely had a glimpse. The differences there are far greater than you imagine, more so than between these two spheres Alex and they wait for you, for all." She bid him farewell.

Alex knew it was time to look for his friends, those whose help he needed for the rescue work he had consciously resigned himself to do.

Chapter 7

Friends Old and New

Alex sat back and thought about the sphere he was in and about the countless shadings in between these and the Divine Spiritual Centre where the Divine Spirit lived. It seemed odd to have a Divine Spirit in a place of its own. Then he realised that this wasn't in any sense true. God was everywhere; there were places God seemed nearer. "For God is within, Alex, within." A thought was with him. Alex said aloud: "Yes, but where, where within?" The answer came: "Seek and ye shall find."

He meditated and realised this drew him nearer. "Oh dear," he said aloud, "so near and yet so far." Someone laughed inside his mind, a beautiful, knowing, loving laugh and it faded gently away.

Alex thought about the library, about the books and passages within them. Certain ones came back more forcefully until he realised that the meanings were not fully noted.

He compared it to listening to an old favourite record and simply *discovering* there were notes and the odd musical phrase which had lain dormant, or never before been heard.

His train of thought led him to a particular book. The poem within was entitled 'SUMMERLAND' and he recalled it word for word:

Oh, knight in armour shining bright
In the throng of battle fight, you cut me down without spite.
You came charging down on me and many of your enemy.
Cutting those within your sight.
Not caring if it's wrong or right, you serve your king with all your
might.

And now I hear the battle fade and find myself in curious haze
I see my loved one there, tiny waist, long flaxen hair,
She'll take me where?
I know not, to a land I once forgot.

So soon the battle cry is gone
And we step forward on and on.
And priceless beauties greet the eye,
Under the never ending blue sky.

Where beauty and love abounds, where life and everything is grand
Welcome to the SUMMERLAND.
For here you'll stay for just awhile
To rest and linger and learn and smile

This place with untold beauty abounds,
as you walk its park-like grounds.
Shining buildings, with spires and steeples
Mixing there with all your peoples.

And one day you meet your knight and greet each other
as brothers one.

Now one great truth has dawned, your rising,
(As the endless morn) on the golden pathway, slowly rising
To greater truths and beauty amazing
For all the sights you've seen right there
There's none at all that can compare,
With all the sights you'll now see there.

And as your journey continues on
Till the day you hear the song and find suddenly that you long,
For something, but you know not what.
And your mind finds past disgraces
and the old familiar places

And you'll find on one cold morn,
That you have once again been born,
Into a world of ugliness and blight.

And once again you meet your knight
And now he holds a wondrous sight
For to her on this cold morn a beautiful child is born,
And once more the cycle is complete
How many times did you meet?

In this cold place, with reckless action and disgrace.
And tho` you know, you cannot tell
You cannot read or write or spell and by the time you can,
Most will have forgotten to a man.

This endless story goes on and on,
Is this a poem or a song? A story true, I tell you dear,
And now the ending is here.

Alex thought about it and realised it told the story of life itself. Of being born, living (on Earth). "This cold place, with reckless action and disgrace." The act of killing and dying, of finding forgiveness in the Spirit World.

Descriptions of spheres and progression through them until the dawning of lessons yet to be learned and birthing again with the final act of Karmic Law playing its part by making one the guardian of the other.

It showed the interplay of the Law of Karma and Cause and Effect in a simple yet direct way. The more Alex thought about it the more interplay between words and phrases he found.

"Ah yes," he sighed, "the simple truths of Spirit simply told. A small still pool with depths beguiling and immeasurable."

He decided he must read more and made his way to the library. He went to a section of books on mediums and mediumship. The section was particularly extensive.

Alex read and read. Knowing nothing would ever be forgotten, he scanned the pages and chapters, gleaning information from every book he turned to until he had, for now, assimilated enough.

He turned and walked quietly, thoughtfully toward the main door and the steps. Outside he glanced around at the groups of people. One in particular drew his attention, a tall slim man around thirty-five with wispy, gingery hair. His gaze met Alex's whereupon his angular features broke into a broad, broad grin.

He appeared in front of Alex. "So there you are, at last my friend, at last." Alex had become used to odd happenings. He studied the man.

"He obviously knows me," thought Alex, "but I can't quite place him." "I'm Desmond," said the man, holding out his hand, "I'm sooo pleased to meet you."

Alex shook hands, still uncertain where they met. "I've waited sooo long, sooo long for this to begin." "Yes," said Alex, "I'm sorry.... but have we met?" "Oh no, but you were described to me and I knew I would know you when we met. We have so much to do together, things are going to be just greaaat," said Desmond.

He had a way of hanging onto words which Alex liked. He felt a comradeship which was special. "I'm Alex," he proudly said, "and I am verrry pleased to meet you."

They sat under a nearby tree exchanging experiences of life, death and learning. Within a space they knew each other very well. Alex learned there would be a group of four and a guide or overseer for their work, one who would be co-ordinating the projects and undertakings. One who would be in direct contact with a group above them.

Desmond had passed in an accident with a lorry. He recalled: "It was stupid really. Should never have been where I was, should have been miles away. Wrong place, wrong time," he said with a wink. Alex knew there was never a wrong place or time, only the right time. Something agreed before birth, sometimes brought forward.

"There I was minding my own business when I comes across a bit o' bovver, an incident like. Dis blokes 'aving trouble wiv 'e's lorry in't he? So being a bit nosey like, we gets chatting and before you knows it I'm 'elping wiv 'e's problem.

"Well I never did drive meself, but there I am giving this direction and that, soo interested in what I'm doing and there 'e is backing up nicely wiv me behind and blow me, don't I jus back into a lamppost!

First fing I knows, I bump the post an' 'e bumps me! Don't that beat all? Well I tries to revive meself but it's no good, then this other bloke comes along an sez: 'Looks like you got a bit ov bovver,' an 'e sez: 'You better give it up mate, best ov a bad job that.'

"Well, I was real confused like...'cause there's me on the pavement an there's me talking to dis bloke. An 'e, jus sez: 'Come on mate there's nuffing to do ere. You jus come wiv me.' An orf we goes and well you no' the rest."

Alex found him an intriguing character. He thought it funny that when communicating our thoughts of our last life to either our loved ones on Earth or reliving, as Desmond just did, that our old habits surface, just as he had brought his old uniform to the meeting, entirely subconsciously.

"We are going to work well together Desmond, I know it. I can feel it," said Alex. They made their way to where Desmond lived, to meet his friends and acquaintances. Alex sent a thought to Maria, who acknowledged it happily.

More and more time was being devoted by Alex to learning. The more knowledge he acquired the less it seemed like *new* knowledge. It seemed more as though he was rediscovering rather than discovering. Less and less he was surprised at what he found. He realised that this was a sign of an old soul, of *knowing* things he hadn't gone out of his way to learn. Lectures, books and friends. The more he communicated the more he found he knew. Slowly the group emerged until at last the four stood together - Alex, Des, Alicia and Jeffrey. All different characters with one aim in common, to serve.

It was at their usual meeting place that the first contact by the overseer was made. They had been discussing various problems around their respective families when a clear thought addressed them all. "May the Divine Spirit bless you all."

82

The interruption brought peace, tranquillity and most of all... love. It was an expression of thought that was tangible; they felt the love that was sent - warm, glowing and comforting. They replied as though with one voice: "Good friend, may the Divine Spirit bless you also, we have been waiting for you."

The thought came again: "You have all been chosen, this you know. Your work is not easy but it is rewarding. At times great difficulties will beset you. Know that I am always here, no harm will befall you.

"Great courage at times will be needed. Know that you have been chosen for your tasks because the qualities required you have in abundance. Know also that many are your guardians and servants and that we are most proud of your commitment to service. It is great work you do and much will come of it."

"One thing must be borne in mind that is most important. Much of your work will bring difficulties for each of you to face. You must remember that these are not only learning processes but also an ordeal by fire.

"It is your purification, the tempering of your metal, for through service lies the path ahead. Progression is there my friends, for those unselfish enough to serve, whatever the face of adversity.

"I know some of you are thinking of my name; it is of no real value. You shall know me by my spirit, by the love I have for you all. I have watched you for eons; serving you is my pleasure, pride and joy.

"Wherever or whenever you work I shall be with each of you; know you need only think of me for help to be at hand. My friends, our work begins, I shall take you to a place of despair, of gloom, for you to be of use to your fellow beings."

They found themselves at what resembled an old quarry. The warmth and brightness of the Summerland had gone. It was cold and overcast. In the air hung the presence of something miserable and forlorn. Alex looked around. It reminded him of a bleak Winter's day. "But on Earth at least they have a beauty of their own," he thought. "No beauty here. Only blight."

Jeffrey ran over to a mound and looked over. There was a long drop the other side and a twisting pathway leading off around a bend in the distance. He knew instinctively. "This way," he said to the others. Unsure of themselves and unfamiliar territory, they thought themselves to points in front and quickly made their way to a small camp where people in rags sat and talked.

Others were trying to cook a meal over an open fire. In the background, some squealing or screaming could be heard. The four looked at each other, wondering what they might do. "Onward, onward," came the thought. They took comfort from the love and moved on.

Beside some broken down huts, they came across two men, one in his late fifties, the other looking nearer his eighties. Both looked like tramps. Their manner and appearance was foul. They sat upon two stools, glaring at each other. The younger was the first to speak: "You've been stealing my food again," he roared, "where have you put it?" "Taint' ad it," replied the other in a deliberate attempt to annoy. "Well, no other bugger's 'ad it." "Now, how do you know that?" smiled the other, showing rotten black teeth.

"I know it's you, it's always you," said the first. "Never stole a thing in my life," came the quick reply. "Did, you had it last time." "Never did," said the elder. Tempers quickly rose and a knife was drawn by the elder, who slashed frenziedly at the face and chest of the other. The squabbling screams of pain and anger stirred a soul nearby.

"Oh no, not again." The thought was picked up. Focussing their attention, they traced it to a small cave behind one of the huts. Inside it lay the huddled shape of an old woman, her stinking rags and matted hair more resembling an animal than a human being. Before Alex could step forward, Des spoke to her in a way she understood. "Bleeding awful init?" he said, thrusting his thumb over his shoulder at the commotion. She looked up, anger in her eyes: "What?" "Bleeding racket," he repeated, "you jus can't ave a bit of kip, can yer?" She sat up staring. He continued: "If dey wanna kill each a'ver dey should do it somewhere else. No wot I mean? Give us a bit of peace, ay?"

"Peace? Peace?" she screamed, "won't find none 'ere love. You'll be lucky not to get beaten or mugged round 'ere at least every day." "So why don't y'go?" said Desmond. A huge rasping cackle gave way to a laugh.

"Go...go where? You must 'ave 'ad yer 'ead cracked once too often," she laughed, wheezing and coughing "Go somewhere else," she said to herself, cackling away, "go somewhere else, thas a good un!"

"Well if y'don't wanna go thas up to you," said Des, taunting her. "Go where?" she said suspiciously. "I know a place but you gotta wanna go," said Desmond. "I aint never seen a place round 'ere," she said cackling away.

"It aint round 'ere and it's really not that far, least we got clothes," he said, pointing to his own. "Huh! Soon 'ave dem off yer back," came the scathing reply. "No, no, dey was given me," said Desmond. "Given ya? Given ya? You're a bloody liar to boot!" she screamed. "No, they were given to all of us," Desmond said. She glanced round furtively.

"Well," she thought, "not kings and queens but better dressed than I is. You all come from this place den?" she questioned. "Yeah," replied Des, "and it's a bit more peaceful and lighter."

LIGHT. It struck a chord within. For a second it registered and the five found themselves on a sunny bank, the old lady being greeted by a loving relative and taken away.

"That," said Des, "was, if you pardon the pun, dead easy." Alicia and Jeffrey joined in the laughter. "That one was", thought Alex. He was remembering the old castle. "Do not worry my friend, GOD is with you," came the thought.

Alex bade the others farewell. A thought had reached him. Urgent, despairing. He followed it through until he found himself at a house he had never seen before.

Through a wall he heard his mother's grief stricken voice: "Don't worry Mary, we just have to pray, ask for God's help. We can only do that. We can do no more. You have done your best."

His mum was cuddling the other woman, whose despair and depression had given way to tears. Her grief hung like a low black cloud, clinging to her and the room. It contrasted starkly with his mother's bright light, whose love and compassion shone like the sun through the clouds.

"There, there, you just let it all out. Don't be afraid or embarrassed just let it all go," said his mother. It was a short time before the woman calmed down.

Drinking some tea, his mother carried on: "We can only go so far you know, we bring our children up as best we can, show them right from wrong but we cannot live their lives for them. They must live their own. We can't blame ourselves for what they do, we can only guide. Our duty is to show them the way and leave the rest to consciences - theirs and ours."

She was talking rather sternly but the truth of it was there, Alex new. "Yes," said Mary, "but my heart bleeds for him, for what he is doing, for what will happen I..."

"You must listen to me Mary, she said, "he must wrestle with his conscience for the pain he puts you through." "Words are so fine," Mary explained, "but don't you understand? He has no conscience! His only love is himself. He has got away with things in the past, it just makes him worse. I don't believe there is a God, to make me suffer like this. There is no justice. None, none at all."

It was all Alex's mum could do to comfort her. Alex looked deep within her, her soul was desolate. "Poor Mary," he thought, she needs rest and healing."

Alex was joined by her relatives, who quickly explained the situation to him. Her eldest son was nothing short of an idiot - irresponsible, immature. A young soul born into that world, like an only child who never learnt to share. Everything was there for him alone and if he could not have it, nobody else would either. This body was built on envy. The cruellest cut of all. It fed his obsession to be *IT - the* one.

If there was a fashion he must have it. If he did not then he was a worthless human being. If you were not dressed *right* in labelled clothes or not had the *in* car then you were not worth the dust you walked on.

In his eyes you were only worth what the fickle minions thought you were. He was truly, as Alex could see, an unhappy soul, posing, waiting to be loved for himself not for his designer clothes.

86

A shallow person surrounded by shallow personalities, guided (like a bull by its ring) by the whim of fashion. Here was Alex's dilemma, to bring comfort and guidance to all.

His mother's voice broke into his thoughts: "Look Mary, you have done all you can. He knows he hurts you. Shall we say a prayer?" Mary nodded and they both kneeled down and began with the Lord's Prayer. This helped them to relax before his mum continued: "Dear God, I know you are aware of our troubles and goodness knows there are plenty worse off than our own. Lots of people sick and dying, others starving or fighting wars. Things that make our own troubles often seem trifle in comparison.

"But, Great Father, we ask you now to help not solely for ourselves but for Joe, who seems bent on causing misery all round. Great Father guide him, for all our sakes. We shall try to be good.

"Dear Father, we send up our thoughts and love and ask for your healing for all our family and friends and ask, as always, that your will be done...AMEN."

"That's a nice prayer," thought Alex, "Mum must have been to more churches." Both he and Mary's relatives sent their loving thoughts, which were tangibly felt.

"You know something," Mary said, "I feel better now and think God may answer our prayers." "Wel, you never know," said Alex's mum, "thank you God," came her private thoughts, "and God bless you Alex, wherever you are."

He gave his mum's hand a squeeze. It went unnoticed. "Now," said Alex, "for the matter in hand." He did not know this boy, Joe, or for that matter his mother's friend; the two had met sometime after his passing, brought together by Spirit for the benefit and progression of each other.

However, Alex did not need to know this *Joe* because, as in absent healing, it was the connection from the person asking (the healer) to the one being asked for, that was followed. The healer or circle need never know anything but a name.

Alex followed the thoughts to the young man, who was fairly well built. "Typical," said Alex, as he surveyed the posing, designer-clothed twenty-two-year-old leaning against his open topped car.

"Bet if it was fashionable to hang brightly coloured beads from ear to ear under your chin, he'd be the first to have it," thought Alex. Joe's ego surrounded him like a brick wall. There he leaned, surveying all his kingdom, radio blasting, doors open for effect, diet drink in one hand, mobile phone the size of half a brick in the other. "Yes, that's right Cathy, I'll pick you up in an hour. I'm not far away now, I'm on the mobile," said Joe, the last phrase being shouted over the radio for the benefit of the peasants, whilst furtively looking around to make sure everybody had noticed the big 'I AM.'

"What a pillock," said Alex to himself loudly. He couldn't help laughing. No more than ten yards away was a pay phone but, to cap it all, Joe had dialled any number and had paid dearer for the call, to which a confused recipient queried the "crossed line?"

"If only he could see himself," said Alex thoughtfully. "He can't," said a voice. It was a guide of Joe's. "All he can see is what he thinks others want, his narrow field of view hides or blurs everything else. He is deeply insecure. He wants to be noticed, loved, but most of all envied.

"It is, I believe, the root of all evil. It makes people materialistic. They strive for what others appear to have. To get it, they work themselves to ill health or death, or worse; they lie, cheat, steal and murder for it, selling their own bodies, or others, by way of prostitution or drug abuse. Most of all they delude themselves that they are having more of what they believe everybody else wants whether it is fun, money or power and all is changed at a whim.

"Did you know that the country squire look is in?" continued the man, "that before long everybody must have some kind of a jeep? Otherwise they will, to use a term, not have street credibility. Can you believe that? Half of these people have not seen a real wild forest or open land, yet they must have the trappings that go with it and will even drive through mud to put on the vehicle to 'show' that they have been 'cross country!'

"I really don't know what the old place is coming to. I know its progressing but sometimes it just doesn't seem like it, does it?" "Sometimes," murmured Alex, who was watching Joe combing his hair yet again while trying to spot any likely girls in his mirror.

Joe stood up, put on the obligatory 'shades,' leaned over and flipped in a tape. The few seconds' relief before the music sounded again were used for impact. The heads that hadn't turned because they thought they had suddenly gone deaf turned at the sound of doors slamming.

He checked his mirror. Yes, most were looking. He smiled a big cheesy smile. "Bet all of them wish they could afford this car," he thought, forgetting it was still being paid for by way of a loan.

The music stung out and with a mandatory spin of the wheels, he was away. Alex and his newfound friend sat in the back as Joe continually flouted speed limits and red lights, cutting from one lane to another whenever it seemed someone might be going faster.

"He always drives like this," said the guide; who introduced himself as Adrian. "It's really quite amazing; there's a little red car behind us who's been there for about four miles. He's keeping to the speed limit, obeying all the rules of the road and our lad's still no further in front. All he does is use more petrol, causes more stress to himself and everyone else and wastes his time." "Not to mention wear and tear on the car," added Alex.

"Exactly," Adrian agreed, "trouble is he uses the boot instead of the head." This made Alex roar: "Yes, I see what you mean." They rode on for a little while until Adrian became pensive.

Alex asked if anything was wrong. "No," came the reply, "not yet." A little further on they came to some lights and the second side of the cassette had just burst into life. The car beside Joe held a couple and their two small children, one of which had woken rudely to the music and started crying.

Joe smiled. They knew he was here. The other driver's look said it all. Joe smiled sweetly at him. The other mouthed: "Effing arsehole" at him. Joe blew him a kiss and pulled away at amber. A second screech of tyres warned him the other driver was not about to let it go. Ahead the road turned into a dual carriageway, speed limit fifty. Joe glanced at his speedo. "Huh," he said to himself, "only doing seventy, plenty of power yet."

Behind him a car was catching up fast. It pulled into the lane beside him, slowly drawing closer. "Is that all it can do?" Joe said aloud and edged the accelerator down, just keeping a few feet in front. He checked his mirror, flipped the wheel to his left, crossing into a line of traffic and stamped on the brake as the other car overran him. Standing on the accelerator again, he cruised past the car, a big cheesy smile and two fingers completed the manoeuvre as he cut back in front.

The other driver was by now fuming. The wife and kids screaming: "For God's sake Dave, stop, stop Dave... Dave!" "Shut your bloody mouth, that arsehole's going to get what he deserves," Dave screamed. "Dave, please stop, please!" his wife screamed again.

Joe looked in his mirror. He could see what was happening and laughed. He lifted the accelerator slightly, just enough to slow him down. "No problem here he thought, I can easily outrun that old bugger." Edging toward him, the other car came up behind. Joe stood on the brakes again and the car behind swerved, trying to get between him and a lorry. Joe pulled away again, playing cat and mouse with four people's lives. Ahead the road narrowed to one lane. Neck and neck they egged each other on. Joe wasn't mad, he was having fun. The other driver was furiously frustrated at every turn.

Joe played with the pedal, speeding up and slowing down to keep the other driver wound up. Together they tore toward the narrowing road, the other driver watching more intently the smiling face in the mirror than the road. Suddenly he saw it narrow on his side. Joe would not let him pass, instead cutting him up. The man braked hard. The screech of tyres giving way to the blaring of horns. Joe put his hand above his head and waved bye bye. Dave fumed... and sweated, so did the wife and kids, but mostly they were frightened.

"That bastard tried to kill us," Dave said. She looked at him: "You tried to kill us." It struck home. "You should have ignored him," tears welled up in her eyes, "please, I want to go home." "But we were going shopp..." Dave was interrupted. "I just want to go home," she said.

Alex was just beginning to realise what sort of idiot he was linking with when Adrian's thoughts butted in: "Just normal behaviour, for him that is. But there are many like him." Alex had felt the sensitivity or psychic link between the two drivers which fuelled the emotions. He found it very interesting and promised to explore it further.

He said goodbye to Adrian knowing they would undoubtedly meet again and made his way back to the others. For a time he sat and considered what had happened. The action and thought forms produced by all concerned, the interplay of all the senses psychic and so-called human. He considered it all, carefully.

He came to the conclusion that souls were being born, retaining more sensitivity on average than at other times; that a change at a preconceived time had begun. He was not sure when it had happened. He scanned his own memories of his last and previous lives and those of friends, realising that children were still childish at sixteen during the sixties, but now they were streetwise at eight or nine.

Not only had they matured quicker, the violence of life, hardship, abuse, sex, of their own sphere of experience was far greater in a shorter time than those of previous generations.

He knew we were all born for experience, but why a quickening of pace? A thought reached him interpenetrating his own: "Because a soul matures with experience, toward the end of its incarnation, it knows and understands more of life. God's own children must experience more, to mature quicker, to lend a greater part of their experience for the fruition of their gifts, so that a more useful life is led in terms of understanding, compassion and love.

"A greater world is emerging from within the Earth and within all souls. Understanding of all things spiritual and psychic is surfacing and with the connection to God, the greater being."

Alex thanked them for their message and brought to mind an old saying particular to the older generation: "If only I knew then what I know now, life would be so different."

Alex's conclusion drew him to the fact that the sensitivities within these souls (which had not been realised by many) were creating these difficulties by the interplay of emotions on a level they could not understand. The realisation that an awareness was required to bring this to light wasn't an earth-shattering one, but how could this be achieved?

"Hello Alex," a familiar voice greeted him. "Bless you Maria," said Alex, still deep in thought. "Its being achieved," another thought. "Pardon?" he replied. "An awareness of people on Earth," came the reply. "But how?" he questioned.

"Through modern science, churches, books, alternative practices and..." she said pausing, "...films. These are reaching a wider audience and the type of films implying an Afterlife are growing. I do not mean the horror ones, those will always exist. There are gentler ones and comedies that are in fashion. They make people think. There are also documentaries.

"Things are being done to stimulate the mind in all fields but most important is the fact that whatever science and *learned* men have tried to deny, people know through their own experiences. More and more have this realisation. The process cannot be reversed. Alex, God's will is being done!"

This gladdened Alex. He now saw things in a different light; it opened a new world to him. An awareness through the most powerful of mediums. Television, books and films.

"Of course, if people insist on being led by the nose, a means of leading them will be found. If fashion conscience people insist on being *into* this film and that, or this idea or that, then Spirit will use that way through. Simplicity itself," thought Alex.

He could see an awareness of the Earth was fashionable through various movements and also an awareness of the plight of animals. "Pollution is now a large issue," he thought to himself.

He wondered how he could affect a quickening of pace. He went to a dome of truth with this question. He learned that many influential people, film directors, scriptwriters and novelists were being inspired to produce works of varying degrees and that much had been accomplished.

As Maria had said, these things had become popular. It was now in fashion to produce and see these films. "A film of just the right calibre is to be produced, for the first time reaching a mass audience, a whole generation, giving the first real glimpse, making them think and enquire. This," said the voice, "will be real progress.

"For the first time people will enquire en masse about their private feelings. About how they affect the world. About what they have done with their lives, but most importantly, what they have done to improve their lives and those of the people around them. It will be a time of reconciliation between all peoples and countries. Nothing stirs the mind like the thought that inner secrets shall be revealed, borne out. It is a sobering thought.

"People shall think more of the consequences of their actions. Once this knowledge is obtained you shall pay double the price for ignoring it."

Alex could see why mediums and such like who used their gifts for self-esteem and gain would need to worry, especially those who took for granted the stupidity of individuals and pandered to their tastes.

Alex took comfort from the fact that all would have an inkling or awareness of the true state of things. "That," he said aloud, "is a real tangible sign of progression. Let those who ignore do so at their peril."

He could see that such a change would indeed have far-reaching consequences. It brought to mind a verse: "Blessed are the meek: for they will inherit the earth." Before, it had meant little to him, he had to be honest, but now it seemed as though it would soon be within grasp.

The real beauty of the Earth and all its glories seen, all nations together. It's a wonderful dream and with the passing of time, to become a reality.

He stepped outside of the dome and thought of his own small part in this intricate scheme of things. Somehow, the day was brighter and he had the feeling of satisfaction, as though he'd seen a good job of work through to the end. But this surely was not the end? No, but a period of learning was over.

He found the others and a discussion arose on their work and things in general. A 'call' alerted them to the fact that someone was in need of help. They found themselves on the lower planes where a woman, one who thought of herself as "one of high regard," needed help. She was extremely well dressed although the clothes were becoming dingy.

The home was luxurious, obviously something she had become accustomed to and did not wish to leave. At first, she mistook Alicia for a housemaid. "My dear young woman, where on earth have you been? I have been calling for ages.

"I'm sure I don't know where anybody is these days, the butler has run off. It's so hard to get reliable help these days. Well, girl, will you answer?" Alicia assumed the role quickly: "Well maam, I've been cleaning the house an...."

"Nonsense girl, I can see dust everywhere and my clothes just seem to have disappeared, the only one I can get is the gardener, the garden looks exquisite." She came back to her point: "Well, where have you been? No lies now, I shall not stand for it."

"Truly maam, I have been cleaning, it's just so big I can't cope on my own," Alicia replied. "Yes, well, I can see it would be troublesome, we must advertise for more staff, I will dictate a letter." This was done.

A discussion followed on the merits of employees, especially of *knowing one's place;* the others left Alicia to it, help being only a thought away should it be required.

Jeffrey was drawn toward the Earth plane where a young man was found to be Earthbound. He had been riding in cars and trains and looking at the existences near to him. He had got used to people not seeing him. Somehow, he was missed by his loved ones and therefore remained in the place he knew best. He liked the bright lights in the city; it made him feel comfortable.

Jeffrey sat beside him on the bus. "All right then mate?" he questioned. "W... Why yes," came the startled reply. It was sometime since anyone addressed him directly. "It's nice this, isn't it? Riding on the bus I mean," saif Jeffrey.

"It's all right," came the reply, "nothing special." "Oh, it's something I haven't done for ages," continued Jeffrey, "I don't visit here very often, I prefer the Spirit World and it can be very depressing here and lonely."

The young man started to think; he knew he was dead but didn't realise there might be more. "Wouldn't you prefer to be with your family?" asked Jeffrey. He said he would but couldn't find them.

"It's no good just looking, you need to call," advised Jeffrey. An old lady got on the bus. Jeffrey winked at her. "Scuse me sonny," she said to the young man, "haven't we met before?"

He looked. "Well blow me down, hello Gran, what are you doing here?" "I've come to take you home my love, Grandad's waiting, so's your uncles and aunts and Blackie."

"Blackie! Here?" She replied: "Well, not here, he's waiting at home, come on, we'll go and see them and you can have a nice cup of tea and a chat."

She took his hand and he passed out as they went up. He came round being led by the hand to a small neat house where friends and relatives had gathered and of course, the dog.

Alicia had spent some considerable time with Mrs Fosdyke, who had a sharp mind... and a fixed one. The home she loved was beginning to look shabby and no matter how she tried, it wouldn't stay clean. "If this carries on," she said sadly, "one will be forced to do one's own repairs. It really is an awful mess; people are so unreliable these days."

Any argument or idea put forward was resoundly sent packing with a dismissive: "You put those silly thoughts out of your head young lady, it really won't do."

Her logical mind would not accept something which to her was: "Totally illogical, utter nonsense." Alicia decided that for now she must leave Mrs Fosdyke to fathom things out alone.

Desmond was attending a road crash; several people had been hurt, three badly. A middle-aged woman and her mother were beginning to vibrate within their bodies. A third middle-aged man was just a few minutes from the change.

The mother appeared first beside her body. She stood watching as it shook in its death throes, her face grimacing then relaxing as the silver thread or cord between them disintegrated.

As the nerves shook the body finally, she looked up at her daughter, whose etheric and spirit body rose above her Earthly one then tilted upright as she opened her eyes. She went to help her mother (the body) and tried to shake her. Her mother came behind and put a loving arm around her. She looked at both forms, hardly able to take it in.

Her mother spoke: "It's all right my love, it's all right." "What about my beautiful baby? My beautiful little girl?" said the daughter.

Their loved ones arrived and intervened: "She's okay, she'll survive. We can see her later but for now we must go home." The bemused younger lady and her mother were led away to a sphere they were to call home.

Desmond watched the man who was fading fast. Help had now arrived in the form of two ambulances and the police. As usual, the sightseers were gathering. A quick look by the ambulance crew told them they could do with more help. A message was radioed out. Screams could be heard amongst the wreckage. Cries and moans filled the air.

An ambulance man ran over to a tangled, crushed Metro. A quick look inside told him these two were past help. A child lay on the back seat unconscious. He checked her pulse and waved to his partner: "Joyce! Over here, a child." She hurried over. "Don't worry about the other two they've had it."

He rushed to the other cars. A man was trapped by his legs, screaming in dreadful agony. The second crew began working. Next, he found the man who was quickly losing his fight. He checked him. "Jesus, this one's close," he thought. "Over here, quick," he beckoned to a colleague.

The body shimmered and vibrated as it freed itself. The man watched as they attempted to get him out in a last desperate hope. It was all or nothing.

The man turned to Desmond and smiled, nodding his head towards his body: "It's a bit of a rum do in't it?" "Yes, I suppose it is," agreed Des.

The man stood passively around as the crew tried to revive him. In a second he was back in his body, sucked in by a strong physical force. A few seconds later he appeared again: "Not having much luck are they? I bet it's been a pig of a day!"

He leaned against the car and checked his watch. "Won't be long now," he said. "Right, one last try," said the leading crewman. The man waved goodbye to Desmond and was immediately sucked back into his body, which now grimaced in pain.

"Right, we've got him," said a crewman, "let's hope we keep him." Desmond didn't think they would have much trouble.

A policeman came over to the Metro: "Did you say two fatals here?" He stuck his head through the empty windscreen frame. "Yea, but there could be a third, it's touch and go though," said his colleague.

"Bleeding drunk drivers. They really piss me off. Licence to kill, that's all it is and I expect he got off lightly." His colleague replied. "I don't think so, he's trapped by the legs. If they don't cut them off here they may have to later."

"Well serves the bastard right. It's all these poor sods I feel sorry for. All this anguish and pain. Just 'cos that selfish bastard wants a drink." "Well, you know how it is," said the other man. "Yeah, I know exactly how it is," replied his colleague. You got the feeling he did too.

Alex and the others all met on their favourite spot. It was a quiet meadow with a group of trees overhanging a small pool with a fountain. Alex was bathing himself, Alicia was talking: "So, I think if we leave her for a little while she'll come round. She's already dissatisfied with what she has and she'll begin to ask questions, it shouldn't be long now."

They had been working fairly hard recently and thought that soon they would take a rest to recuperate. Rest in the Summerland really meant doing something else as, unless you're new, it wasn't really necessary. They each had their own projects and interests. Things which they were unable to pursue on Earth for one reason or another.

An urgent call came from the overseer. Their help was desperately required to attend to some helpers in the lower regions. A fear rose in Alex; he knew this would be unpleasant. They found themselves in a grey shadowland. The light similar to evening or nightfall.

The smell of fear and rot and decay was odious. In the distance they could see some lights. "There, there," shouted Desmond. Quickly they made their way.

Three helpers were struggling with some of the inhabitants who were holding back a poor soul whose spark of humanity had been lit.

The four rushed to help. "So the cavalry has arrived!" jeered one. "Well, we have help as well!" Within seconds creatures scuttled from holes and pits. One came flying through the air landing on Alex's back clinging tight. The stench was awful, like rotting flesh and it tore at him.

The others couldn't attempt a rescue as they too were being attacked. Before Alex a huge man-shaped form beckoned him forward with knarled, misshapen fingers, more reminiscent of claws.

Alex found himself being manhandled towards this figure slowly and surely by three accomplices and struggle as he might, he could not resist their combined force.

Thoughts were penetrating his mind, not allowing him to think. Savage, blood-curdling things. Thoughts of all kinds. Of bestial things which they obviously delighted in portraying.

Fear now rose in Alex. Now he was beginning to play their game. His mind became confused, cloudy. He was being hurt, just for pleasure. He glanced round. The others were having a frightful time also, with their private fears and horrors being expanded upon.

The being in front of Alex produced a long blade: "Do you know what I am going to do with this?" he cackled and snarled repulsively.

The words conjured up hideous pictures. Just what they wanted. "I save up special things for the likes of you," the hideous cackle rose to hysterical laughter as he slashed Alex's chest.

"Some very special tricks," he poked Alex savagely "Just" poke, "for" poke, "you." His hot stinking breath made Alex gag. "Oh God, If ever I need help, I need it now," thought Alex.

The thought went out, strong and clear. In the background, he heard screaming. Someone was being torn limb from limb. His thought went out: "Paul, help us."

A bright light appeared in the gloom, which sent some of the creatures scuttling away. Others held him tightly. Paul walked toward Alex and stopping a few feet away, held out his hand: "Come, they cannot hurt you."

He struggled against their restraint: "I can't move," Alex said fearfully. "You can, rise above them. Do not join their thoughts. Remember what you are, send them your love," replied Paul.

The words encouraged Alex. His knowledge and lessons slowly came back. Slowly his light, which had dimmed considerably, began to resume its vigour. The creature's grip began to loosen. His light grew stronger.

"Alex, you need have no fear, you always have Love. Yea, even though you walk through the valley of death," said Paul. Those words reminded Alex of The Truth.

Alex walked toward him and together they approached the others, each being released in turn. Their attention was drawn to a cowering shape, huddled and frightened on the ground. Frightened as much of the newcomers as of his 'Old friends.'

Alex walked across. "Come on my friend, your place is with us." It did not move; Fear had frozen its bedraggled form. "Rise, my friend, no harm will befall you." Alex knelt down and took it gently by the arms, helping it to stand.

It hung its head in shame, for what it was, for what it had become. "Do not be afraid, we have come to help you," said Alex. The eyes stared up. A familiarity struck Alex. Something in the eyes.

The face was torn, misshapen and bloated. Totally unrecognisable but the eyes showed something. He smiled at the creature: "Your safe with us, don't worry."

The small spark of understanding that had attracted so much attention grew a little brighter. A humble and frightened: "Thank you" greeted Alex's ear. It was a Scot's accent. "We've come to take you home James," he said.

They appeared at a ward. It was different to the one Alex was used to. This had walls and a ceiling. "It was," explained a gentleman in charge, "to provide a feeling of security for the patients."

James McArdle would need a lot of looking after. Alex sent him his love and healing. Poor James, he had been through a lot. He would go through a lot more.

A change had come over Alex, he somehow felt different, uncomfortable in some sort of way yet brighter, happier. "Well hello," said a familiar voice, "and how are you?"

"Fine, just fine. I've been attending to an old friend," said Alex. "So I see." "He's had a tough time for the last seven or eight years," Alex replied.

"I know and now you've brought him home." "Yes, thank God." "And I have come to take you home." Maria smiled her beautiful smile, "Well done Alex."

Chapter 8

Home Again

Alex liked his new home and quickly became accustomed to it. It was more beautiful than ever he had imagined, much more so than the previous glimpse had led him to believe. He realised that the feeling of uncomfortableness was in fact the result of his vibration being lifted; the lower vibration no longer suited him, just as it had been on his visit to his new home with Maria.

He noticed the change had instilled in him a longing. To further his work, to do more for others. His love of others would drive him on relentlessly, so he could bring others to that which he had achieved.

His frequent journeys to the Summerland drew all kinds of people toward him. At times, he found he took on the role of teacher to those souls around him. This gave him great satisfaction.

He kept a close eye on James, mostly from a distance, his progression being hindered by overpowering thoughts. James had been used to getting his way, to having what he wanted and now everything was given freely, in love. He found it hard to come to terms with it; his mind still believing that force was the reason for the gifts.

The four had taken their rest. Desmond and Alicia learnt music and dance. These were things they had always wanted to do; however, their times on Earth had given little opportunity for various reasons.

Jeffrey was very interested in the science of healing. Should he ever incarnate again, he wanted to be a surgeon - if the chance be permitted. He read extensively, attended lectures and courses and saw surgeons of all kinds working. Frequently he visited Earth hospitals to see particular operations being carried out.

The call to work was, for some, long awaited but it came sure enough, as they knew it would. Alex joined the others at their favourite spot in the Summerland, followed shortly by the overseer.

They were given their instructions and formed a ring of light. Immediately they found themselves in a tunnel. Within seconds a tube train passed them, followed by an almighty crash.

Alex was still impressed by the timing of these occasions. They each had been given names and descriptions of those to pass. Their job was to make sure no soul wandered off away from loved ones who came to meet them. In particular, a rather selfish and materialistic woman.

The friends and relations had also been present at the moment of each passing and all went well except, as expected, this woman. It seemed to Alex she had, for some reason, been bludgeoned into a dreamlike state. She was completely unaware as to her surroundings. It was almost a dreamstate, but no intervention from Alex or any others had any effect. Although completely free of her body, she drew herself to it.

Alex likened this to a drunk who comes round clutching a lamppost; the knowledge of how they arrived there is completely zero but the familiarity brings comfort and so they hang on, trying to clear the mind before taking another step.

Any outside help remained unnoticed. For Alex, it was a disappointment; he felt he had missed his chance but the overseer gave comfort: "The shock has focused her thoughts onto those things which are familiar, those which gave her greatest comfort. For now, there is little we can do. Her mind has always been dominated by material things and therefore she seeks these now. Say a prayer Alex, then we must leave. We can do nothing for the time being."

They left immediately, Alex seeking answers to questions that arose. His thoughts were interrupted by a cry of help; it drew him to his parents' house.

His father was having a heart attack, his mother was struggling with the phone. "Yes, that's right, an ambulance, please come quickly," she gave the address.

As Alex looked on, his father's bodies were beginning to loosen and separate. An Uncle and grandparent came, they greeted Alex: "Not long now," said the grandmother, her hands clasped in front of her, the love radiating in all directions, the gentleness of her soul reflecting in her smile.

The bodies began to vibrate and swiftly his father joined them, his attention first drawn to his grandmother. "Oh Nana!" said Alex's father. "Yes, it's me and Joel is here also." Joel came into focus and together they lifted him upward.

Alex's mother was cradling the head: "Oh come on, come on, please hurry, for God's sake hurry." Deep down she knew the ambulance would arrive late, but she still kept hoping, ignoring signs of death.

Alex sent her love and healing. He understood she needed to go through this; his father had now begun anew and she would need to find the strength to cope.

Some twenty minutes later, a knock sounded at the door, but it only registered at the back of her mind. Her thoughts were with her husband, memories distant and close. She knew by now he was gone; her experience of the churches gave her strength, even so it was a shock, but she knew he had gone on to a better place.

Her tears were also tears of relief, knowing it was a quick passing. "Better that than a long illness, God has been kind," she said. She sent her thanks: "Great Father, let me always ask, whatever comes, Thy will be done."

Frantic knocking at the door brought her round, a voice was shouting through the letterbox. She called back and went slowly to the door. The ambulance crew came in and confirmed what she already knew. They made their way silently to the hospital, Alex continuing to send his thoughts while his mother sat as though entranced. The second great love of her life had gone and now she felt alone.

Three or four hours passed quickly until she found herself at home. It felt as though she were just coming round, waking perhaps from a dream, perhaps a nightmare.

She put down the cup she held and raced into the kitchen where the chairs and crockery lay sprawled and she knew it was true.

Alex's own passing had affected her deeply but he had been spared the attraction of her grief through firstly having been rested deeply and secondly by his understanding and interaction with her, which was to a degree special. It had also been cushioned by her newfound love and support from her husband.

This last bridge had gone. Good friends gave their support, so did her faith but the circumstances were now different and the feelings exaggerated by the loneliness she felt. She was pining for her husband, pulling at him.

This caused great hindrance to his father, who at times was distracted not only from his work but also from recovery. He often felt unable to wrench himself away from her, her grief surrounding them both, smothering any progression.

Alex found any contact immediately brought memories and melancholy and a plan was devised to get her to a medium, who would explain the situation to her.

The months passed and the time came when she found herself once again at a church. "You have been fretting my dear, haven't you? About a recent passing, four to five month's ago, yes dear," the medium said.

Alex found the medium's voice irritating, especially all those "*yes dears.*" Her guides joked; it's all right for you, you may only hear it for tonight, we have to work with her all the time."

Most guides had a sense of humour. "God knows, they need it sometimes," said Alex quietly to himself. He listened again. "You're holding him back dear, he knows you love him, but he's gone on to a better place. He says that nothing has really changed; he's just gone into the next room as it were. This grief is doing neither of you any good, you both have lives to live, do you understand?" the medium went on.

Alex's mother nodded as though she understood. "He says you're not taking it in my dear, he doesn't love you any less, in fact he can show his love in a greater way, but your grief is a barrier to him, pulling him and you away from progression but also keeping him within a certain distance, do you understand this?" the medium continued.

Again, Alex's mother nodded. Alex intervened. "Someone called Alex is helping you both but you must give yourself a chance. Be happy in the knowledge that a great love is there. He will show himself when he is able but the conditions must be right and you are hampering them. He says you have grieved enough - 'rest yourself easy.' I'm told to tell you that your knowledge will return my dear, God bless," and with that the medium finished.

A spark had now been rekindled and the spell broken. His mother's experiences now came slowly back, comforting her but also giving her a sadness, for the lessons previously learned had been temporarily thrown by the wayside but realising she had learnt a greater lesson - primarily, how easy it is to cut yourself off in grief, to engross yourself within your own world, even with the knowledge. She now had compassion and understanding for others in the same position and she cried a happy tear, for she knew she was fortunate enough to be shown the way and therefore to be able to guide others also. Her faith was now reinforced to a greater degree by God's goodness. His love had shown her how to help others and in thanksgiving she promised that she would help given the chance, whenever she could.

Alex still marvels at the intricacy of HIS works; how the lessons are learnt by experience, which is ultimately the reason for incarnation. For merely reading a set of rules is far different to living them and his mother's lesson taught him many things too. Alex and the others were becoming more involved in the new world order which was soon to be established.

It had been talked about by the higher guides for at least two centuries beforehand and now a great excitement rose in those who were aware, both in Spirit and incarnate.

Children were being born with a knowledge and awareness of the true state of things, born of all cultures and races. These children would grow to be more tolerant of others to *fine-tune* the societies in which they live.

Alex knew also that a halt had been called to new and newer souls being born; the reason for this is simple: Those who are inexperienced sow trouble. Not the kind that benefits, but the kind that hinders; those ones who wreak havoc for the sake of it. He remembered Joe. He knew only too well that a last opportunity lay before those who cast themselves with the dark side to gain what they could.

Trouble would ensue before final peace set in. Alex knew that natural disasters would also occur, forcing people to re-examine their relationship with God. For it is those disasters which focus Man's mind on the infinitesimal effect he has on the natural ways of this world. All the technology cannot stop a hurricane or earthquake or famine.

Man can only be aware of its impending progression; he can only deal with its after effects. This he does with great effort and often more concern for his own individual well-being than for others.

A different type of mediumship was to arise; a different way of working, new techniques and most of all, new types of mediums with their own ways of working. An explosion of mediums would ensue, heralding the dawn of the new age. Yes, problems would occur undoubtedly, but for the majority, good work was to follow.

The failure of orthodox medicine would focus attention upon the alternatives and modern medicine would slowly relinquish its hold on its minions, gradually accepting, then supporting, its old adversaries. This, together with the combined weight of other similar pressures, would herald finally the dawn of a new and finer age for Mankind, an age where there is acknowledgement that there is a universal being (whichever name we wish to give it), one that acknowledges that we all have personal responsibility for our actions and thoughts.

His head began to swim. The excitement had risen so far in him that his vibration began to hover at a pace which was quite unsuitable. This brought him back to reality with a bump.

He decided to visit some friends who had held a circle for the last four years, all who could be termed young mediums from thirty to forty years of age.

Although Alex knew the five members very well, they did not know him, by name at least; he was very much behind the scenes. Mediumship seemed to be gearing itself to something approaching trance.

There was to be more direct contact between guides and well-wishers with a message and those termed 'recipients.' Overshadowing and transfiguration would play a part.

Once the acceptance of those things were generally held in the world then philosophy and messages, with deeper meanings, would take over from platform and private sittings. Real help with real problems, truly helping those in need to see the light, showing why the difficulties they were encountering had to be faced, why it was Karmic and how they would benefit. They would also be shown (if it were deemed necessary at the time) the reason for this present incarnation.

Tonight was to be special, for the trance state was to be extended. The medium had already given permission and although a little nervous, was sure in the comfort and experience of friends.

The meeting opened with the usual prayers and thanks which helped them to 'open up,' preparing for work. Four concentrated their love and power onto the last, who took, for what all the world looked like, a fitful sleep.

Alex watched as the guides began shaking and coaxing the medium gently out of his body, chemicals playing a large part. It had previously been explained to Alex that some individuals had a great deal of these chemicals naturally and could *free* themselves at will (it was a different process to Astral Projection).

Outside his body, the medium stood very still and reminiscent of sleep state, would remember very little. His guide moved in closer to the seated body from behind to *absorb* this gross material.

Alex could not really appreciate the difficulty that this problem posed and after a short talk was given by the guide, he was invited to try; the circumstances most unusual but he decided to have a go.

As he drew closer it felt very strange, everything began to slow down like a film in slow motion. As he lowered his vibration, his mind seemed hardly to function at all.

Within seconds Alex felt a 'clunk' as he settled in. The arms felt heavy, like lead weights. It was a great effort to move even the eyelids. He attempted to produce a sound from the voice box and try as he might, it produced only gurgling sounds.

The whole experience made him decidedly uneasy. He was suffocating in a living tomb, like a parasite being starved of air. It was too much for him and he exited rather sharply, which made the medium 'snap' back into his body with a jolt and made him rather ill.

For Alex, it was too much like being incarnated or born. The heaviness of the body brought back too many memories for him. There was a distinct alienation in being incarnate. It wasn't something he wanted.

There was a longing to progress above it, to not have the need, but he knew there was little chance of not incarnating again as he had so much to learn.

He realised, of course, that a great many did so for very special reasons (Christ being one), sometimes the needs of others surprisingly not figuring highest in the calculation (not applying to Christ). They incarnate to bring about a specific purpose, to influence a particular moment in history and having made their mark, disappear.

This brought to mind Abraham Lincoln and the emancipation of the slaves. A great step forward for Humankind. It was a little known fact that Abraham Lincoln had an interest in mediums and had met at least two. On being given specific information and proof, he devised his strategy. It was, Alex knew, divulged in a book of which there were only a few copies on Earth (Alex of course had watched the play).

He wondered that so much effort (of being born, training, struggling and studying to achieve a certain position) be concentrated on what so often be conjectured to be a 'chance' meeting, one that was predestined long before either are born. One that could or would have such an impact upon the world, such was the work of Spirit. God has infinite patience and wisdom. His very soul reaches into our world. God does work in mysterious ways.

Alex now thought of the great men and women now prevalent on Earth, many struggling against darker forces, influencing those who have a craving for power, greed and self-gratification.

He thought to himself: "Ah well, such is the struggle of life." He sat at his favourite spot, considering all that had been set in motion by this one experience. Food for thought indeed. It made him consider whether there would be a need for him to incarnate again. He sincerely hoped not, but this was for purely selfish reasons. He hated the conditions of Earth and loved those he found here.

A thought interpenetrated his: "You have done many things for God, would you not do this if it were asked of you?"

He acknowledged instantly. "Do you not realise that though you may leave these lands for the blinking of an eye, you would return to a greater world?" He acknowledged this also.

"Then child, have no fear, the great love is with you always." He felt ashamed at his lack of courage and understanding. He knew he would not be any further from God and any trials set could and would be beaten.

He felt his acknowledgements had in some sense given permission for trials yet to come. He pondered the reason for this progression when the answer came.

"There comes a point in progression where the way forward can only be cleared by enduring another life on Earth. Gradually (if the spirit is unwilling) it is made to see that this is the only way ahead.

"It then chooses, or is helped to choose, the most beneficial path for the particular qualities it must needs have. When agreement is reached with its guides and mentors, a time is set with the parents (whose paths have also been set out).

"The spirit is present at inception; it becomes acquainted with the form produced. It is totally aware of the parents' feelings, especially the mother's. It frequently visits the embryo, taking longer passages of time with each visit. From the World of Spirit, it seems remarkably like a dream or form of sleep.

"With the passing of time the position reverses so that the spirit feels more at home or 'alive' in the body, with less and less contact with the World of Spirit, that then seeming more like a dream.

"When the time for the birth approaches, the spirit is 'imprisoned' within the body (this can be hours before the birth), very seldom is it left until birth itself. This being the final sealing of its fate, encased in a gross living tomb. Great mourning is felt by its friends in Spirit, such as we mourn a death.

"However, joy is also felt, knowing that progression is open to that soul in a unique way and knowledge that it will soon be home, a little purer, cleaner and amongst friends once again and because of this, 'a little closer to God.'"

Alex thanked them for their advice. He now began to understand the way of things from a different perspective, as though all sides were shown, for the particles of truth be forged into one truth.

All these perspectives were necessary to gain a complete picture. Now he realised he had, of course, given consent to the incarnation which gave him his present name and through study, discovered others.

Experience beautifies the soul for no lesson is ever wasted. Each and every part forms the whole, rather like a television picture made up from tiny dots.

As the months and years passed, his understanding grew and grew. He became a guide to a young man who became a fine medium and Alex's involvement taught him many things.

In repayment of a Karmic debt, he incarnated to a young couple knowing he would pass over or return within two months time.

It was for him a very moving experience. A debt repaid with lessons learned on all sides, plus the experience of incarnating with a great knowledge of Spirit retained.

The birth itself was difficult and because of his knowledge, he was allowed to enter the chosen form in the last few minutes. A farewell was arranged with friends, family, guides and teachers.

At the last few seconds a panic entered him but to no avail, his consent had been given.

The movement was involuntary (rather like exit), he was sucked swiftly and forcefully into the body to land with a sudden 'bump,' exactly as when you arrive back in your body during sleep, waking with a sudden jolt.

He joined a short time before birth, taking note of the light and sounds that could be heard outside the womb and also the comforting whooshing and bump, bump noises within his mother's body.

The journey through the birth canal into the harsh light of a cool restless world signalled his arrival as a healthy baby girl, thrust unceremoniously into a material world.

This, together with a swift smack, brought all his emotions to the fore. For the two months before the passing, which added yet another statistic to cot deaths, he found communication vastly infuriating and frustrating, this being virtually limited to crying (which happened frequently) or not crying. The passing was quick and easy, being signalled by the pre-arranged arrival of a friend to take him from a body he barely knew.

110

His arrival back to Spirit taught him many things, especially how invaluable that last incarnation had been, however short its duration.

He knew now that for him it was to be his last incarnation on Earth; that his work lay spread before him.

Service to others, service to all, in love, through guidance, through teaching, through sacrifice, through help. But most of all, THROUGH GOD.

About Leo Bonomo

The Author, Leo Bonomo, was born in Forest Gate London in 1957. From a very early age Leo had always 'seen and heard things,' in fact it was so normal that Leo assumed that everybody else saw them too.

'Astral Projection' or 'Out of the Body' experiences were one of the phenomena he could produce at will, most of the time. Leo assumed also that everybody else did it too. This was until an incident at school made him realise that this was 'not normal;' the result was that this gift was stopped immediately. There are many experiences to be told that would fill another book!

Leo trained as a medium for approximately eight years at the SAGB (Spiritualist Association of Great Britain) and spent some years touring churches and giving readings. Leo was the very first student to give private readings at the SAGB and had associated with many fine mediums who worked there at the time.

Leo was also an active member at the SAGB for a number of years; he was a member of the council and was invited, with the change of the old regime at that time, to become president of the association, which typically for him, he modestly let the opportunity go. Various incidents and happenings eventually induced him to step back from his work.

Until the time was ready, he was asked again to work for Spirit and to publish the books and poems he channelled. Leo has also been on TV for a series of interviews and demonstrations for Circle TV. Part of 'TheCircle' is a 'Psychic Line.' He has also been interviewed on radio in September 2012 and was interviewed on Felixstowe TV in 2013. He continues to be involved in a small way with media.

Leo would like to sincerely thank Harry Shapiro and Caesar Glebbeek for their excellent book 'Jimi Hendrix Electric Gypsy.'

Regretfully, the Jimi Hendrix Estate withheld permission for the soundtracks to be added and the reprinting of Jimi's lyrics, which would have made this book complete. You are however, encouraged to listen to his works, especially those tracks that have been mentioned. There is a short list of recommended listening.

Jimi himself was interested in spiritual things, not surprisingly, as he was, on his grandmothers side, part Cherokee Indian - The Cherokee Indians, the Yun Wiya, the Real People, were thought by other tribes to have come from the skies. There a lot of Native American Indian Guides helping Mediums. They were and are a very spiritual people.

In private, some of those close to Jimi knew how devoted he was to the spiritual aspects of life.

In public life, Jimi was very much on his guard, well aware that there are those who would ridicule and even destroy the careers of those who speak of such things. Even so, there are times when Jimi was seen to be pushing the boundaries.

However, there are now programmes like 'Jimi Hendrix – The Uncut Story' where many who knew of Jimi's great spiritual power now talk openly about it. It seems that now is the time for this to be explored. For Leo, this knowledge was there from his early introduction to Jimi.

Jimi told *NME:* "I dream a lot and I put a lot of dreams down as songs." He would later tell friends how, as a child, feeling detached from the real world because nothing in the real world was secure enough to hold on to, he would lie in bed and somehow find himself floating away, looking down at himself, knowing he wasn't asleep, but drifting through the mists of another dimension - the Astral plane, looking for something he could never identify.

Jimi took part in a film/concert called 'Rainbow Bridge.' 'Rainbow Bridge' was a Psychic Research Centre, or Occult Centre. Jimi was involved in various things while he was there. During the film Jimi talks of some of his experiences.

This is a transcript from part of the film 'Rainbow Bridge'. It features Jimi Hendrix's interview where he talks about some of his experiences of 'Astral Projection' and I believe of how he wrote or had the inspiration for his classic song 'Machine Gun,' but you must make up your own minds. Jimi is asked a direct question from someone he is sitting in a circle with:

"Do you ever get the feeling that you have been totally out of your body? Actually going somewhere? And not taking your body with it? Outer space? You been?" Jimi: "Yeah." "Where do you go when you go?" Jimi: " I don't know that, it seems like this little centre in space, that it's rotating, constantly rotating and there's these souls on it and like you're just sitting there like 'as cattle at a water hole' there's no rap actually going on, there's no emotions strung out actually, you know, next thing then you know you be drawn to a certain thing and all of a sudden, like, it's bright and you see yourself being the page, being turned and see yourself next to a Vietna... er soldier being cut down, you arrive on the scene as it were, everything is beautiful, lush green, brighter than day... Blair witches... and like you see it completely crystal, scene of a soldier being shot down. All of sudden you see yourself helping that soldier up, not... not his uniform but you're feeling yourself delving, another vibe, another sense of that soldier, seems like his soul and then you whisk back to the water hole of the oasis of the souls."

Those of us with a little understanding, or are 'experienced,' know that Jimi is describing an 'Out Of The Body Experience' or 'Astral Projection,' where he has witnessed the scene he talks about. You would then understand that this scene has been transposed into the brilliant song 'MACHINE GUN.'

'Rainbow Bridge' is the closest that Jimi has ever come to publicly speaking, not of only the writing techniques he sometimes used, but his personal beliefs and direct experiences.

Once you understand that then listen to the song, ony then can you only begin to understand how Jimi relives the pain, anguish and feeling of the moment of that death, when he plays the song live (the very best version is the one on the 'Band of Gypsys' album). No wonder his songs have so much impact. This is what makes them timeless, the impact and the heartrending emotions he tears out of them and the listener.

Jimi had also given a fifteen minute interview in which he tells of his coming death (I believe this is parodied by 'Angel'). It is on the B-side of a vinyl record, which Leo foolishly did not buy many years ago and has regretted ever since. The Jimi Hendrix Estate has denied that such a record of this interview has ever existed. Leo would be most grateful to anyone who may be able to provide him with a copy.

Listen again to 'Band of Gypsys.' When Jimi introduces the song 'Machine Gun,' he says: "Happy new year first of all... forget about me, not too many more of them around...," then, to lighten the mood, " if we can get over the summer that is." As you may know this was the last Christmas Jimi had.

Leo's thanks go to Eric Clapton and Carlos Santana, whose quotes are also reprinted.

Eric Clapton said that: "You could tell when Jimi was playing best, he did not appear to there at all, it's what musician's dream of. The moment when you and your instrument are one and the notes just flow."

This interview was originally published in UniVibes' issue 17, February 1995. © UniVibes 1995 - reprinted by permission of UniVibes, International Jimi Hendrix Magazine, Coppeen, Enniskeane, County Cork, Republic Of Ireland:

"Carlos Santana needs little introduction. His appearance at the original Woodstock festival in 1969 and at Woodstock II in 1994 is testament to his longevity as a musician."

"**UniVibes:** You introduced Jimi Hendrix's step-sister Janie on stage at Woodstock II - is she a musician?"

"**Carlos Santana:** Not that I know of. I know she just wanted to get something off her chest and we allowed her the opportunity to do so, and we felt very honoured to share the stage with her. The whole sky was grey most of the time but when we got to that portion of the presentation, when she came onstage, it was like one of those Walt Disney movies where this brush appears in the sky and then all the sky turns from grey into golden pink peach, kinda like a cloud. We went 'woah', you know. And there was specifically one cloud that just stood in front and it looked like an angel - it had the wings and everything. Everybody noticed it, you know - this was all happening while she was crystalizing her views on where Jimi's music is today and what needs to be done for her to rescue the music from the lawyers."

"**UV:** Have you got a favourite Hendrix song or album?"

"**CS:** I think all the first three are still my favourites like anybody else. The first three albums by Jimi - it was like being captured and put into a space ship and they take you on a trip and

115

they bring you back instead of like jumping in a Mercedes or a Rolls Royce. I especially always like it when Jimi Hendrix would play the song and then he go on to, uh, Chainsaw Massacre Tazmanian Devil Aurora Borealis Galaxy - I like it when he start with the feedback. And I saw Stevie Ray do it one time too. I'm sure he did it many times but I only saw him do it one time were he where the guitar became like an Aurora Borealis and all this colours of sound were screaming out of it even though he wasn't putting his fingers on it. That's kinda like invoking ghosts or something and that's my favourite part that I miss about Jimi is when he would open up certain channels and let certain demons and angels dance together, you know what I mean - that it was beyond 'B' flat or 'C' flat. That's when it's music to me. Anybody can play music just like anybody can think. Very few people are conscious and very few people can do something beyond the note. So thank God that Jimi had that kind of spirit that...the foundation was the blues but he also was a very cosmic person [laughs]. You know to this day I haven't heard anybody... I mean, I heard a lot of people pick up what Jimi completed or he was doing but I haven't heard anybody complete it or really pick it up. Not only from the volume or the approach to the sound or the tone but the philosophy behind it... Jimi didn't just play like that because he could strangle a Stratocaster or a Marshall, he played like that because he saw it a certain way and he took certain things that made his spirit be stronger upon his playing. Otherwise, anyone could do it - you just pick it up, lift it off from the CDs, you know, or the records. No, you had to have some kind of thing like the Blues Brothers' mission from God or something, you know. But you have to have some kind of inner fueling, inner anger or inner passion, some kind of really, really emotional spill-over on your playing otherwise it won't sound like that even if he had the same amplifier and the same guitar and everything - it still won't sound that way. I crave to try to create an album that basically goes that way, more like Sun Ra and Sonny Sharrock and Jimi Hendrix, you know, with a little bit of lyrics and very little vocals but mainly the electric guitar and the Hammond organ and the congas. Tell stories of interplanetary or galactical or celestial time rather than just earth time. I think that's what Jimi Hendrix used to call 'Sky Church Music'."

Recommendations

Recommended Hendrix Listening Tracks:
Drifting, Belly Button Window, Star Spangled Banner, 'Machine Gun, Are You Experienced?, Angel, 1983 (A Merman I Should Turn To Be), Gypsy Boy, Third Stone from the Sun, Purple Haze, Hey Baby (New Rising Sun), Axis: Bold as Love, Little Wing.

Recommended Books:
• 'Testimony of Light' – Helen Greaves.
("One of the best books I have ever read." Leo)
• 'Voices In The Dark' – Leslie Flint - *My Life as a Medium, As told to Doreen Montgomery*
• 'In the Dawn Beyond Death' – The Rev. Charles Drayton Thomas.
• 'Silver Birch' series of books – Silver Birch was a Spirit Guide who spoke through the medium Maurice Barbanell.
• 'The History of Spiritualism' – Sir Arthur Conan Doyle.
• 'The Curse of Ignorance' – Arthur Findlay.
• 'On the Edge of the Etheric' – Arthur Findlay.
• 'Life In The World Unseen' – Anthony Borgia.
• 'Science and Psychic Phenomena: The Fall of the House of Skeptics,' 'Science and the Near-Death Experience' and 'Science and the Afterlife Experience' – Chris Carter.

Should you ever doubt that negative spirits can influence for the worst then these are two books you should read! Remember! Untrained people should not use the Ouija board:
• 'Spiritism and Mental Health' and 'Resources for Extraordinary Healing' – Emma Bragdon, PhD, Director Spiritual Alliances, LLC Director of Foundation for Energy Therapies, Inc.
• 'Thirty Years Among The Dead' – Dr Carl Wickland.
In each of the above are cautionary tales of the result of dabbling with Spirit. Should you have an interest, you need an inspired, development teacher. Leo's book, 'Training for Mediumship – Using the New Energies,' will be published shortly. Its guidance is invaluable in finding a good teacher and what you should expect and how you should develop as a medium.

Recommended Websites:

www.leo-bonomo.com

www.robertbrown-medium.com
Robert Brown, who Leo met at SAGB. Robert is an excellent Medium, internationally renowned.

www.emmabragdon.com
Dr Bragdon's book 'Spiritism and Mental Health' is highly recommended.

www.scienceandpsychicphenomena.com
For Chris Carter.

www.leslieflint.com
This site contains a few of the thousands of recordings this excellent medium has produced. The tapes contain actual conversations and guidance from those in Spirit. Many are famous names; lots are just 'ordinary people' and all have interesting stories to tell. Leslie is the most tested medium ever. No one has ever been able to prove that his extraordinary gift is not genuine. From ordinary people to royalty, many have sat with him and been astounded by Leslie's extraordinary gift.

Author's Notes

This book, that was channelled and completed in 1987, has some prophecies in it, some of which have already come to pass. Others have yet to come true; these are for the reader to discover.

Some are now obvious, like the proliferation of Spirit orientated programmes, films and the like, which are now thankfully so prevalent that they mostly do, however, regrettably, err on the side of the dark.

I am sure that you can see programmes like 'The Vampire Diaries' that are occult-based, that have great following and while they touch on the subject, have no enlightenment about it. This is not a criticism of the programmes themselves, it is what it is and reflects to a degree what the public wants.

Spirit, however, would prefer that a lighter reflection of the truth be given, showing that so many good things can happen and of course there are an array of programmes and films that reflect this too. Unless you are connected (to Spirit), how could you understand that these things would come about and be so very popular?

Spirit work, with what they have as far as Earthly things are concerned, will always find a way and so many things have changed. These things are popular by design; there is a purpose about them and the change that is necessary now is the change that brings the light. Wouldn't it be wonderful if something, Disney like, made up in a film, showing such magical things, miraculously turned out to be miraculously true?

There is no limit to what we can do, more for others than ourselves. Having read this book, there is no turning back, a door has been opened, hastened by the change in vibration and we have all chosen to be here, at this time, for a specific reason.

This is still a place of learning, it is its reason for being here, but now we can, should we choose to learn of the better things in life and to put away that fear of passing, knowing that when we do we can perform our own miracles daily and truly make this world a better place.

Light, always,

Leo

The picture above is of Leo, aged approximately nine, in the
garden in Forest Gate.
Leo was born in 1957, making the year approximately 1966.
In the background, you can see, standing, his grandfather.
Some can also see a woman to his grandfather's left.
Leo's grandfather passed away in 1933.